Israel's Money and Medals

Arnold H. Kagan

Published under license by
American Israel Numismatic Association, Ltd.

Editor
Sylvia Haffner Magnus

AMERICAN ISRAEL NUMISMATIC ASSOCIATION, INC.

Founded in 1967, the American Israel Numismatic Association has now grown to include thousands of members from countries all over the world. Dedicated to the advancement of the knowledge of ancient and modern Israel coins, medals and numismatic items, the Association's affiliated clubs have conducted hundreds of meetings and issued thousands of mailings. AINA regularly publishes a scholarly publication, THE SHEKEL in order to increase the knowledge of its members and to provide a forum in which members and friends may meet and exchange views with fellow collectors. The Association has affiliated clubs in most large cities of the U.S. and Canada and serves individual members through a variety of mail services plus an annual AINA convention, seminars at most other major numismatic events and an annual study tour to Israel. If you seek to benefit from the knowledge and lore of Israel's numismatics, you are invited to join.

Inquiries should be directed to:
P.O. Box 25790
Tamarac, Florida 33320

ACKNOWLEDGEMENTS

We wish to thank the Israel Government Coins and Medals Corporation, its director Mr. Eliezer Shiloni and the Deputy Managing Director, Mr. Israel Zadaka for the valuable assistance given to us in the preparation of this supplement. We have made extensive use of their prospectuses, catalogues and photographs. Our gratitude to Sandy Roth, the Head of Operations in North America for all services rendered on our behalf.

Mr. S. Aviezer, Assistant Director of the Currency Department of the Bank of Israel... a SPECIAL thanks for keeping us informed on all of the new issues, mintage figures, photographs... and for taking the time to point out all of the errors and omissions of the previous supplement.

DEDICATION

TO THE COLLECTOR...

Dear Collector:

Another supplement to the 1982 supplement... we really planned a new edition... but circumstances led to this 2nd Supplement. A full edition will be forthcoming in two years.

You see... the book is getting so large we had to make a decision on just how to publish a full new edition. We have decided to print the new edition on pre-punched pages... with all chapters numbered with their own code number. Future supplement pages will then be able to be inserted into their individual chapters WITHOUT changing the page numbers.

The loose-leaf covers will be sold separately... therefore... you may choose to make two volumes. One for all coins and banknotes and one for all medals.

If you find any errors, omissions or inconsistencies, please advise the editor so all corrections may be included in the full edition. A special thanks to Morty Zerder for his assistance.

Thank you for your continued interest. We will always try to keep you up to date on the continuing developments in Israel's Money and Medals.

Enjoy...

Sylvia Haffner Magnus

Sylvia Haffner Magnus

Dear Friend,

We are proud that American Israel Numismatic Association is now publishing "Israel's Money and Medals." This new supplement includes material issued by the Bank of Israel, the Israel Government Coins & Medals Corporation, and American Israel Numismatic Association. American Israel Numismatic Association is honored in having the international responsibility for bringing this new information update to collectors around the world.

Since 1976 American Israel Numismatic Association has been dedicated to its members, and to the advancement of knowledge of ancient and modern Israel coins, medals, banknotes and other numismatic items.

Sylvia Haffner Magnus, Editor of this book, seeks to bring to the reader the most comprehensive and up to date material available, making it an invaluable guide to the collector. Sylvia has an eye for detail and a mind for marshalling data; she also contributes to The Shekel - American Israel Numismatic Association's bi-monthly publication, and is a member of the Board of Directors.

We thank Sylvia for her years of effort on behalf of all of us. We gladly join her on this occasion in making available the latest supplement to a waiting public.

A special "thank you" to Arnold Kagan for publishing the last four editions.

If you seek to benefit from the knowledge and lore of Israel's numismatics, we invite you to join the American Israel Numismatic Association.

Morris Bram

Morris Bram - President
American Israel Numismatic Association, Inc.

Contents

1984 MARKET PRICE VALUES

PRUTA SERIES

		BU
P-1	1948 25 Mils	$1,000.00
P-1a	1948 H-L xf-au	600.00
P-1b	1948 U-F xf-au	350.00
P-2	1949 25 Mils O-L	100.00
P-2a	1949 C-L	25.00
P-2b	1949 S-L	-R-
P-2c	1949 H-L	100.00
P-3	1949 1 Pruta w/p	3.00
P-3a	1949 polished	6.50
P-3b	1949 proof	50.00
P-4	1949 w/o/p	12.00
P-5	1949 5 Prutot w/p	2.00
P-5a	1949 proof	50.00
P-6	1949 w/o/p	9.00
P-7	1949 10 Prutot w/p	40.00
P-7a	1949 proof	75.00
P-8	1949 w/o/p	5.00
P-9	1952 10 Prutot al.	2.00
P-10	1957 10 Prutot al.	2.00
P-11	1957 10 Prutot cea.	2.00
P-12	1949 25 Pruta w/p	2.00
P-12a	1949 proof w/p	50.00
P-13	1949 w/o/p	40.00
P-14	1954 25 Pruta ncs	3.00
P-15	1949 50 Pruta w/p	35.00
P-15a	1949 50 Pruta proof	75.00
P-16	1949 50 Pruta w/o/p	4.00
P-17	1954 50 Pruta m/e	40.00
P-18	1954 50 Pruta p/e	4.00
P-19	1954 50 Pruta ncs	4.00
P-20	1949 100 Pruta w/o/p	3.00
P-20a	1949 100 Pruta proof	75.00
P-21	1955 100 Pruta w/o/p	3.00
P-22	1954 100 Pruta-Berne	3.00
P-23	1954 100 Utrecht xf-au	500.00
P-24	1949 250 Pruta w/p	15.00
P-25	1949 250 Pruta w/o/p	4.00
P-26	1949 250 silver "H"	13.00
P-27	1949 500 Pruta silver	25.00

AGORA SERIES

		BU
A1-1	1960 1 Agora	$10.00
A1-1a	1960 LD xf	450.00
A1-1a/b	1960 LD-DD	-R-

AGORA SERIES CONT'D.

A1-1b	1960 DD xf	$ 35.00
A1-2	1961 1 Agora	9.00
A1-2a	1961 TD xf	40.00
A1-2b	1961 WD xf	30.00
A1-3	1962 1 Agora	.75
A1-3a	1962 SD	20.00
A1-3b	1962 DD	20.00
A1-4	1963 1 Agora	.75
A1-4a	1963 inv.	20.00
A1-5	1964 1 Agora	.50
All others	1965-1980	.15
A5-1	1960 5 Agorot	15.00
A5-2	1961 5 Agorot	2.00
A5-2a	1961 ICI	180.00
A5-3	1962 5 Agorot LD	.50
A5-3a	1962 SD	15.00
A5-4	1963 5 Agorot	.50
A5-5	1964 5 Agorot xf-au	150.00
All others	1965-1980	.20
A10-1	1960 10 Agorot LF	12.00
A10-1a	1960 10 Agorot SF	10.00
A10-2	1961 10 Agorot	9.00
A10-2a	1961 Patcha xf	50.00
A10-3	1962 10 Agorot LD	.75
A10-3a	1962 10 Agorot SD	16.00
A10-4	1963 10 Agorot	.75
A10-5	1964 10 Agorot CS	.75
A10-5a	1964 10 Agorot SS	50.00
All others	1965-1980	.25
A25-1	1960 25 Agorot LF	4.00
A25-1a	1960 25 Agorot SF	4.00
A25-2	1961 25 Agorot	.75
A25-3	1962 25 Agorot	.75
A25-4	1963 25 Agorot	.75
All others	1965-1980	.25
A50-1	1963 ½ Lira LA	10.00
A50-1a	1963 ½ Lira SA	30.00
A50-2	1964 ½ Lira	1.00
All others	1965-1980	.25
A100-1	1963 1 Lira LA	5.00
A100-1a	1963 1 Lira SA	20.00
A100-1b	1963 1 Lira flat-1	20.00
All others	1965-1980	.35
A500-1	1978 5 Lirot	.40
A500-2	1979 5 Lirot	.40

MINT SETS

		BU
MS-1	1962 16 coins	$60.00
MS-2	1963 18 coins	50.00
MS-3	1964 18 coins	35.00
MS-4	1962 6 Prutas-large	25.00
MS-5	1962 6 Prutas-small	20.00
MS-6	1963 white-stapled	125.00
MS-6a	1963 white-card	95.00
MS-6b	1963 wh. Inv. 1 Agora	125.00
MS-7	1963 blue-wh.-card	15.00
MS-7a	1963 Inv. 1 Agora	45.00
MS-8	1965 card	1.50
MS-9	1966 card	1.50
MS-10	1967 card	1.50
MS-11	1968 card	1.50
MS-12	1969 card	2.00
MS-13	1970 card	2.00
MS-13a	1970 wallet	2.00
MS-14	1971 wallet	3.50
MS-14a	1971 plastic	2.50
MS-15	1972 wallet	4.50
MS-15a	1972 plastic	4.50
MS-16	1973 plastic	3.00
MS-17	1974 plastic	3.00
MS-18	1975 plastic	3.50
MS-19	1976 plastic	5.00
MS-20	1977 plastic	6.00
MS-21	1978 plastic	5.00
MS-22	1979 wallet	3.00
MS-22a	1979 plastic	10.00
MS-23	1980 plastic	10.00
MS-23a	1980 plastic-unc set	4.00
MS-24	1981 Piefort	13.00
MS-24a	1981 wallet (Lira)	2.75
MS-25	1982 Piefort	13.00
MS-25a	1982 plastic	4.00
MS-26	1983 Piefort	12.00
MS-26a	1983 plastic	4.00
MS-27	1984 Piefort	11.00

COMMEMORATIVES
HALF-SHEKEL

HS-1	1961	$14.00
HS-1a	1961 proof	32.00
HS-2	1962	10.00
HS-2a	1962 proof	13.00

HANUKKA COINS

H-1	1958 Torah Or	3.00
H-1a	1958 Torah proof	50.00
H-2	1960 Degania	6.00
H-2a	1960 Degania proof	40.00
H-3	1960 Szold	40.00
H-3a	1960 Szold proof	250.00
H-4	1961 Hero	13.00
H-4a	1961 Hero proof	18.00
H-5	1962 Italian Lamp	45.00
H-5a	1962 Italian proof	55.00
H-6	1963 N. Africa Lamp	45.00
H-6a	1963 N. Africa proof	55.00
H-7	1972 Russian Lamp	9.00
H-7a	1972 Russian proof	12.00
H-8	1973 Babylonian L.	8.00
H-8a	1973 Baby. proof	9.00
H-9	1974 Damascus Lamp	8.00
H-9a	1974 Damascus proof	9.00
H-10	1975 Holland Lamp	10.00
H-10a	1975 Holland proof	12.00
H-11	1976 Amer. Lamp	20.00
H-11a	1976 Amer. proof	30.00
H-12	1977 Jerus. Lamp	8.00
H-12a	1977 Jerus. prf. O-M	9.00
H-12b	1977 Jerus. prf. C-M	15.00
H-13	1978 French Lamp	8.00
H-13a	1978 French proof	9.00
H-14	1979 Egyptian Lamp	14.00
H-14a	1979 Egyptian proof	18.00
H-15	1980 Corfu Lamp	24.00
H-15a	1980 Corfu proof	35.00
H-16	1981 Polish Lamp	24.00
H-16a	1981 Polish proof	35.00
H-17	1982 Yemen Lamp	18.00
H-17a	198w Yemen proof	36.00
H-18	1983 Prague Lamp	16.00
H-18a	1983 Prague proof	30.00

ANNIVERSARY COINS

A-1	1958 Menorah	$18.00
A-1a	1958 Men. proof	500.00
A-2	1959 Exiles	30.00
A-2a	1959 Exiles proof	65.00
A-3	1960 Herzl	30.00
A-3a	1960 Herzl proof	65.00
A-4	1961 Bar-Mitzvah	50.00
A-4a	1961 Bar-Mit. proof	90.00
A-5	1962 Negev	85.00
A-5a	1962 Negev proof	95.00
A-6	1963 Seafaring	425.00
A-6a	1963 Seafaring proof	450.00
A-7	1964 Museum	90.00
A-7a	1964 Museum proof	135.00
A-8	1965 Knesset	22.00
A-8a	1965 Knesset proof	27.00
A-9	1966 Life	19.00
A-9a	1966 Life proof	20.00
A-10	1967 Eilat	23.00
A-10a	1967 Eilat proof	30.00
A-11	1968 Jerusalem	21.00
A-11a	1968 Jerus. proof	23.00
A-12	1969 Shalom	20.00
A-12a	1969 Shalom proof	21.00
A-12b	1969 Shalom "kaf"	21.00
A-13	1970 Mikveh	16.00
A-13a	1970 Mikveh proof	17.00
A-14	1971 Science	16.00
A-14a	1971 Science proof	17.00
A-14b	1971 Science "Star"	17.00
A-15	Aviation	16.00
A-15a	Aviation proof	17.00
A-16	1973 Scroll	16.00
A-16a	1973 Scroll proof	17.00
A-17	1974 Revival	16.00
A-17a	1974 Revival proof	17.00
A-18	1975 Bonds	17.00
A-18a	1975 Bonds proof	19.00
A-19	1976 Faith	16.00
A-19a	1976 Faith proof	17.00
A-20	1977 Brotherhood	14.00
A-20a	1977 Brother. proof	15.00
A-21	1978 Loyalty	15.00
A-21a	1978 Loyalty proof	16.00
A-22	1979 Motherhood	17.00

ANNIVERSARY COINS CONT'D.

A-22a	1979 Mother. proof	$22.00
A-23	1980 Peace	27.00
A-23a	1980 Peace proof	38.00
A-24	1981 Book	32.00
A-24a	1981 Book proof	55.00
A-25	1982 Rothschild	25.00
A-25a	1982 Roth. proof	42.00
A-26	1983 Valour	20.00
A-26a	1983 Valour proof	55.00
A-27	1984 Kinsman	22.00
A-27a	1984 Kinsman proof	40.00

PIDYON HABEN COINS

PH-1	1970	17.00
PH-1a	1970 proof	18.00
PH-2	1971	17.00
PH-2a	1971 proof	18.00
PH-3	1972 "star"	17.00
PH-A3	1972 "no star"	25.00
PH-3a	1972 proof	18.00
PH-4	1973	15.00
PH-4a	1973 proof	16.00
PH-5	1974	15.00
PH-5a	1974 proof	16.00
PH-6	1975	15.00
PH-6a	1975 proof	16.00
PH-7	1976	15.00
PH-7a	1976 proof	16.00
PH-8	1977	17.00
PH-8a	1977 proof	18.00

SPECIAL ISSUE COINS

SI-1	1967 Victory	16.00
SI-1a	1967 Victory proof	17.00
SI-2	1971 People	16.00
SI-2	1971 People proof	17.00
SI-2b	1971 People Berne	950.00
SI-3	1974 Ben Gurion	16.00
SI-3a	1974 Ben Gur. proof	17.00
SI-4	1980 Jabotinsky	29.00
SI-4a	1980 Jabot. proof	40.00
SI-5	1982 Qumran ½ Sh.	12.00
SI-5a	1982 Qumran 1 Sh.	30.00
SI-6	1983 Herodian ½Sh.	13.00
SI-6a	1983 Herodian 1 Sh.	27.00

GOLD COINS

G-1	1960 Herzl	$350.00
G-2&3	1962 Weizmann	1075.00
G-4	1954 Bank of Israel	400.00
G-4a	1954 Bank proof	2250.00
G-5	1967 Victory	825.00
G-6	1968 Jerusalem	350.00
G-7	1969 Shalom	325.00
G-8	1971 People	350.00
G-9	1973 Scroll 50 L.	100.00
G-10	1973 Scroll 100 L.	200.00
G-11	1973 Scroll set-3	600.00
G-11a	1973 Sdroll set-2	300.00
G-12	1974 Ben Gurion	325.00
G-13	1975 Israel Bonds	250.00
G-14	1978 Loyalty	250.00
G-15	1980 Peace	350.00
G-16	1980 Jabotinsky	350.00
G-17	1981 People-Book	400.00
G-18	1982 Rothschild	400.00
G-19	1982 Qumran Caves	200.00
G-20	1983 Valour	400.00
G-21	1983 Herodian	210.00
G-22	1984 Kinsman	375.00

GOLD MEDALS
STATE MEDALS

		mm.	
SM-1	Judaea Capta	27	$175.00
SM-12ghj	Bar-Mitzvah	27,22,19	300.00
SM-12r	Bar-Mitzvah	30	200.00
SM-12s	Bar-Mitzvah	22	87.00
SM-12t	Bar-Mitzvah	13	36.00
SM-21efg	Liberation 2	27,22,19	350.00
SM-29c	Terra Sancta	35	250.00
SM-35b	Masada	27	200.00
SM-35h	Masada	22	87.00
SM-38b	Rothschild	35	250.00
SM-41b	Balfour	35	275.00
SM-42b	El Al	35	300.00
SM-43b	Keren Hayesod	35	325.00
SM-48b	Rubinstein 1st	35	575.00
SM-48c	Rubinstein 1st	35	417.00
SM-53b	Technion	35	350.00
SM-54b	Entebbe	35	225.00

GOLD STATE MEDALS CONT'D.

		mm.	
SM-56b	Bat-Mitzvah	30	$200.00
SM-56c	Bat-Mitzvah	22	87.00
SM-56d	Bat-Mitzvah	13	36.00
SM-57b	Wedding	30	200.00
SM-57c	Wedding	22	87.00
SM-57d	Wedding	13	36.00
SM-61c	Egypt-Peace	35	200.00
SM-64c	Shema Yisrael	30	200.00
SM-64d	Shema Yisrael	22	87.00
SM-64e	Shema Yisrael	13	36.00
SM-64f	Shema Yisrael	18	70.00
SM-66b	Holocaust	18	70.00
SM-68b	Jewish Settle.	18	70.00
SM-69b	Honor-Elders	18	70.00
SM-71b	Retirees	18	70.00
SM-72b	It's a Girl	18	70.00
SM-73b	It's a Boy	18	70.00
SM-74b	Am Israel Hai	18	70.00
SM-74c	Am Israel Hai	13	36.00
SM-75b	Tourism	18	70.00
SM-76b	Volunteers	18	70.00
SM-77	Jerusalem-Gold	22	87.00
SM-78b	Blessed-Healer	18	70.00
SM-79a	Resistance-Nazis	18	70.00
SM-81b	23rd Olympics	30	200.00
SM-81c	23rd Olympics	22	87.00
SM-82b	Montefiore	22	87.00

GOLD CITY COIN MEDAL

CCM-9b	Jerusalem	35	350.00

GOLD HOLY LAND MEDALS

HLM-4b	Temple Mt.	22	87.00
HLM-4c	Temple Mt.	13	36.00

GOLD COMMISSIONED MEDALS

CM-8a	Tourism	19	700.00
CM-47c	Chicago Bank	45	3500.00
CM-59b	Maariv	35	450.00
CM-68e	Diamond T-1	35	450.00
CM-68f	Diamond T-11	35	450.00
CM-79d	Hobby T-1	22	300.00
CM-79e	Hobby T-11	22	300.00
CM-80	Chagall	35	1000.00

GOLD COMMISSIONED MEDALS CONT'D.

		mm.	
CM-88b	Iraq Center	35	$850.00
CM-91b	Rubinstein II	35	650.00
CM-98b	Mexico-Israel	30	300.00
CM-98c	Mexico-Israel	38	525.00
CM-105b	Rubinstein III	35	575.00
CM-113b	Iran	40	3000.00

GOLD PRESENTATION MEDALS

PM-3a	Haganah	27	285.00

GOLD A.I.N.A. MEDALS

AM-3d	Bicentennial	38	375.00
AM-9d	13th Anniv.	37	275.00

STATE MEDALS

SM-1a	Judaea Capta	S-30	$25.00
SM-1b	Judaea Capta	C-61	20.00
SM-1c	Judaea Capta	S-61	95.00
SM-1d	Judaea Capta	S-35	35.00
SM-1e	plugs Jud. Cap.	B-59	125.00
SM-1f	plugs Jud. Cap.	S-61	250.00
SM-2	Valour	C-59	13.00
SM-A2	Valour	T-59	10.00
SM-2a	Valour	S-59	85.00
SM-2b	Valour	S-35	35.00
SM-3	B'nai B'rith	C-61	29.00
SM-3a	B'nai B'rith	S-35	40.00
SM-4	Tel-Aviv	B-59	12.00
SM-4a	Tel-Aviv	S-35	30.00
SM-5	Hadassah	B-59	12.00
SM-5a	Hadassah none	S-35	100.00
SM-5b	Hadassah with	S-35	35.00
SM-6	Bar-Cochba	B-59	12.00
SM-6a	Bar-Cochba	S-59	95.00
SM-6b	Bar-Cochba	S-35	30.00
SM-7	Authorities	B-59	35.00
SM-7a	Authorities	S-35	85.00
SM-8	1st Harp	S-35	70.00
SM-9	Pentecostal	B-59	28.00
SM-10	Press Inst.	B-59	29.00
SM-11	Bnei-Beraq	B-59	27.00
SM-12	Bar-Mitzvah	B-59	18.00
SM-12a	Bar-Mitzvah LT	B-59	65.00
SM-12b	Bar-Mitzvah	S-59	115.00
SM-12c	Bar-Mitzvah	S-35	40.00

STATE MEDALS CONT'D.

SM-12d	Bar-Mit. Kaf	S-19	$10.00
SM-12e	Bar-Mit. no-Kaf	S-19	11.00
SM-12k	Bar-Mit.	T-45	10.00
SM-12m	Bar-Mit.	S-45	40.00
SM-12n	Bar-Mit.	T-59	10.00
SM-12p	Bar-Mit.	S-37	35.00
SM-13	Pablo Casals	B-59	28.00
SM-13a	Pablo Casals	S-59	160.00
SM-13b	Pablo Casals	S-35	75.00
SM-14	2nd Bible	B-59	32.00
SM-14a	2nd Bible	S-59	150.00
SM-14b	2nd Bible	S-35	75.00
SM-15	Shavit	B-59	35.00
SM-15a	Shavit	S-59	140.00
SM-15b	Shavit	S-35	75.00
SM-16	Kadman	B-59	32.00
SM-16a	Kadman	S-35	75.00
SM-17	Synagogues	B-59	28.00
SM-18	A-J Congress	B-59	30.00
SM-19	Festival	B-59	35.00
SM-20	2nd Harp	B-59	35.00
SM-21	Liberation 2	B-59	12.00
SM-21a	Liberation 2	S-59	95.00
SM-21b	Liberation 2	S-35	35.00
SM-21c	Liberation 2	S-19	7.00
SM-21j	Liberation 2	T-45	10.00
SM-22	U.J.A.	B-59	32.00
SM-22a	U.J.A.	S-59	310.00
SM-23	H.U.C.	B-59	37.00
SM-24	Ghetto	B-59	15.00
SM-24a	Ghetto	S-59	105.00
SM-25	Tower	B-59	14.00
SM-26	1st ZOA	B-59	24.00
SM-27	3rd Festiv.	T-59	25.00
SM-28	1st Settlers	B-59	14.00
SM-28a	1st Settlers	S-59	110.00
SM-29	Terra Sancta	B-59	14.00
SM-29a	Terra Sancta	S-59	95.00
SM-29b	Terra Sancta	S-35	34.00
SM-30	S.S. Shalom	B-59	30.00
SM-30a	S.S. Shalom	S-59	160.00
SM-30b	S.S. Shalom	S-35	75.00
SM-31	Blockade	B-59	14.00
SM-31a	Blockade	S-59	90.00
SM-31b	Blockade	S-35	35.00

SM-32	Histadrut	B-59	$75.00
SM-33	Tel-Aviv F.	B-59	34.00
SM-34	Chess	T-59	37.00
SM-35	Masada	T-59	18.00
SM-35a	Masada	S-35	45.00
SM-35c	Masada	S-45	40.00
SM-35d	Masada	T-45	10.00
SM-35e	Masada	S-59	125.00
SM-35f	Masada	CN-45	7.00
SM-35g	Masada	S-27	22.00
SM-36	3rd Bible	T-59	14.00
SM-37	Museum	T-45	16.00
SM-37a	Museum	S-45	40.00
SM-38	Rothschild	T-59	13.00
SM-38a	Rothschild	S-45	40.00
SM-39	Sinai	T-59	15.00
SM-39a	Sinai	S-45	50.00
SM-40	J. Legion	T-59	32.00
SM-40a	J. Legion	S-45	135.00
SM-41	Balfour	T-59	13.00
SM-41a	Balfour	S-45	40.00
SM-42	El Al	T-59	14.00
SM-42a	El Al	S-45	40.00
SM-42c	El Al	S-59	160.00
SM-43	K. Hayesod	T-59	12.00
SM-43a	K. Hayesod	S-45	35.00
SM-44	Weizmann	T-59	12.00
SM-44a	Weizmann	S-45	35.00
SM-45	K. Kayemeth	T-59	12.00
SM-45a	K. Kayemeth	S-45	35.00
SM-46	J-Knesset	T-59	12.00
SM-46a	J-Knesset	S-59	90.00
SM-46b	J-Knesset	T-45	11.00
SM-46c	J-Knesset	S-45	45.00
SM-46d	J-Knesset	T-70	12.00
SM-46e	J-Knesset	S-34	29.00
SM-47	25th Anniv.	T-59	10.00
SM-47a	25th Anniv.	S-45	29.00
SM-47b	25th Platinum	P-35	500.00
SM-48	Rubinstein	T-59	11.00
SM-48a	Rubinstein	S-37	30.00
SM-49	Volunteers	T-59	14.00
SM-49a	Volunteers	S-37	30.00
SM-50	Weizmann	T-59	14.00
SM-50a	Weizmann	S-37	32.00
SM-51	Mt. Scopus	T-59	14.00
SM-51a	Mt. Scopus	S-45	40.00
SM-52	Heb. Univ.	T-59	14.00

SM-52a	Heb. Univ.	S-45	$40.00
SM-53	Technion	T-59	14.00
SM-53a	Technion	S-45	40.00
SM-54	Entebbe	T-59	11.00
SM-54a	Entebbe	S-59	85.00
SM-55	Diaspora	T-59	12.00
SM-55a	Diaspora	S-45	45.00
SM-56	Bat-Mitzvah	T-59	12.00
SM-56a	Bat-Mitzvah	S-37	35.00
SM-57	Wedding	T-59	12.00
SM-57a	Wedding	S-37	35.00
SM-58	Habimah	T-59	13.00
SM-58a	Habimah	S-45	45.00
SM-59	S. Zedek	T-59	12.00
SM-59a	S. Zedek	S-45	40.00
SM-60	Einstein	T-59	13.00
SM-60a	Einstein	S-45	40.00
SM-61	Egypt	T-59	12.00
SM-61a	Egypt	S-59	80.00
SM-61b	Egypt	S-45	40.00
SM-62	Pilgrims	T-59	11.00
SM-62a	Pilgrims	S-45	45.00
SM-63	J. Agency	T-59	12.00
SM-64	Shema	T-59	11.00
SM-64a	Shema	S-37	35.00
SM-64b	Shema	S-27	22.00
SM-65	Jabotinsky	T-70	12.00
SM-66	Holocaust	T-59	11.00
SM-66a	Holocaust	S-37	35.00
SM-67	5th Bible	T-59	11.00
SM-68	Jewish Sett.	T-59	11.00
SM-68a	Jewish Sett.	S-34	29.00
SM-69	Elders	T-59	11.00
SM-69a	Elders	S-34	29.00
SM-70	Pidyon Haben	S-34	29.00
SM-71	Retirees	T-59	11.00
SM-71a	Retirees	S-34	29.00
SM-72	It's A Girl	T-59	11.00
SM-72a	It's A Girl	S-34	29.00
SM-73	It's A Boy	T-59	11.00
SM-73a	It's A Boy	S-34	29.00
SM-74	Chai	T-59	11.00
SM-74a	Chai	S-34	29.00
SM-75	Tourism	T-59	11.00
SM-75a	Tourism	S-34	29.00
SM-76	Volunteer	T-59	11.00
SM-76a	Volunteer	S-34	29.00

STATE MEDALS CONT'D.

SM-78	Healer	T-59	$11.00
SM-78a	Healer	S-34	29.00
SM-79	Nazis	CN-45	7.00
SM-80	Purim	S-27	24.00
SM-81	Olympics	T-70	11.00
SM-81a	Olympics	S-37	29.00
SM-81e	Olympics	CN-30	6.00
SM-82	Montefiore	T-59	9.00
SM-82a	Montefiore	S-37	29.00

CITY COIN MEDALS

CCM-1	Ashkelon	T-45	10.00
CCM-1a	Ashkelon	S-45	45.00
CCM-2	Acre	T-45	10.00
CCM-2a	Acre	S-45	45.00
CCM-3	Tiberias	T-45	10.00
CCM-3a	Tiberias	S-45	45.00
CCM-4	Beit She'an	T-45	10.00
CCM-4a	Beit She'an	S-45	45.00
CCM-5	Avdat	T-45	10.00
CCM-5a	Avdat	S-45	45.00
CCM-6	Caesarea	T-45	10.00
CCM-6a	Caesarea	S-45	45.00
CCM-7	Jaffa	T-45	10.00
CCM-7a	Jaffa	S-45	45.00
CCM-8	Lod	T-45	10.00
CCM-8a	Lod	S-45	45.00
CCM-9	Jerusalem	T-45	30.00
CCM-9a	Jerusalem	S-45	45.00

HOLY LAND MEDALS

HLM-1	Jerus. Gates	T-59	10.00
HLM-1a	Jerus. Gates	S-37	37.00
HLM-2	Capernaum	T-59	10.00
HLM-2a	Capernaum	S-37	37.00
HLM-3	Nazareth	T-59	10.00
HLM-3a	Nazareth	S-37	37.00
HLM-4	Temple Mt.	T-59	10.00
HLM-4a	Temple Mt.	S-37	37.00

COMMISSIONED MEDALS

CM-1	B'nai B'rith	C-61	140.00
CM-2A	1st Harp	C-61	150.00

COMMISSIONED MEDALS CONT'D.

CM-2B	1st Harp	B-59	$100.00
CM-3	Hadassah	B-59	650.00
CM-4	Local Authority	B-59	250.00
CM-5	Press Institute	B-59	200.00
CM-6	3rd Casals	B-59	150.00
CM-6a	3rd Casals	S-59	-R-
CM-7	Shavit "Till"	S-59	300.00
CM-7a	Shavit brass	B-59	-R-
CM-8	Tourism	B-59	150.00
CM-8a	Tourism	T-59	110.00
CM-9	H.U.C.	B-59	130.00
CM-10	3rd Festival	B-59	325.00
CM-10a	3rd Festival	SP-59	325.00
CM-11A	Remembrance	B-59	30.00
CM-11B	Remembrance	T-59	30.00
CM-12	Z.O.A. 1st	B-59	95.00
CM-13	Bank-Israel	S-30	125.00
CM-16A	Gideonim	SP-59	375.00
CM-16B	Gideonim	T-59	165.00
CM-17	4th Festival	T-59	15.00
CM-17a	4th Festival	SP-59	15.00
CM-18a	Masada	C-35	225.00
CM-18b	Masada	C-35	315.00
CM-19	Terra Sancta	B-59	95.00
CM-20	B'nai B'rith	T-59	15.00
CM-21	Hebrew Univ.	T-59	15.00
CM-21a	Hebrew Univ.	S-59	90.00
CM-21b	Hebrew Univ.	S-45	-R-
CM-21	Hebrew Univ.	S-45	45.00
CM-22	5th Festival	T-59	12.50
CM-22a	5th Festival	SP-59	13.50
CM-23	Transportation	T-59	12.50
CM-24	Israel Bonds	T-59	350.00
CM-24a	Israel Bonds	S-59	-R-
CM-25	3rd Harp	T-59	95.00
CM-26	Yad Vashem	T-59	400.00
CM-26a	Yad Vashem	S-59	-R-
CM-27	Ashdod Port	T-59	15.00
CM-28	Hod Hasharon	T-59	15.00
CM-29	Israel-Canada	CN-39	6.00
CM-31	2nd Z.O.A.	T-59	15.00
CM-32a	Bank-Isr. Pens.	S-35	250.00
CM-32b	Bank-Isr. Pens.	S-35	350.00
CM-33	Economic Conf.	SP-59	400.00

COMMISSIONED MEDALS CONT'D.

CM-34	Stoke Mand.	T-59	$15.00
CM-34a	Stoke Mand.	SP-59	15.00
CM-34b	Stoke Mand.	GP-59	20.00
CM-34c	Stoke Mand.	T-45	12.50
CM-34d	Stoke Mand.	SP-45	13.50
CM-34e	Stoke Mand.	GP-45	15.00
CM-35	Tefahot Bank	T-45	100.00
CM-35a	Tefahot Bank	S-45	-R-
CM-36	Industrial Bank	T-45	125.00
CM-37	El Al	S-59	150.00
CM-38	4th Bible	T-59	12.50
CM-39	Jerusalem	T-59	100.00
CM-39a	Jerusalem	S-59	800.00
CM-40	4th Harp	T-59	20.00
CM-41	Lottery	T-45	12.00
CM-41a	Lottery	S-45	50.00
CM-42	Dr. Pool	T-59	20.00
CM-42a	Dr. Pool	S-59	100.00
CM-42b	Dr. Pool	S-59	60.00
CM-43	W.I.Z.O.	T-59	15.00
CM-43a	W.I.Z.O.	GP-59	20.00
CM-44	Zim Israel	T-59	15.00
CM-44a	Zim Israel	S-45	55.00
CM-45	Bank of Israel	T-59	65.00
CM-45a	Bank of Israel	S-45	200.00
CM-46	Tel-Aviv Mus.	T-59	15.00
CM-46a	Tel-Aviv Mus.	S-45	65.00
CM-47	Chicago Bank	T-59	250.00
CM-47a	Chicago Bank	S-59	375.00
CM-47b	Chicago Bank	S-45	275.00
CM-48	Israel Ports	T-59	120.00
CM-48a	Israel Ports	S-59	-R-
CM-49	Munich Syn.	S-45	75.00
CM-50	O.R.T.	T-59	20.00
CM-50a	O.R.T.	T-59	15.00
CM-50b	O.R.T.	S-59	450.00
CM-51	Pharmacy	T-59	300.00
CM-51a	Pharmacy	S-59	-R-
CM-52	Zim Service	T-59	20.00
CM-52a	Zim Service	S-45	230.00
CM-52b	Zim Service	S-45	90.00
CM-53	3rd Z.O.A.	T-59	12.50
CM-54	Plastic Surg.	T-59	80.00
CM-54a	Plastic Surg.	S-59	475.00
CM-55	Commerce	T-59	250.00
CM-55a	Commerce	S-59	350.00
CM-56	5th Harp	T-59	12.50

COMMISSIONED MEDALS CONT'D.

CM-57	6th Festival	T-59	$12.50
CM-58	Lawyers	T-59	55.00
CM-59	Maariv	S-35	100.00
CM-59b	Maariv	B-35	35.00
CM-60	Nature	S-45	50.00
CM-62A	Remembrance	T-59	175.00
CM-62B	Remembrance	T-59	275.00
CM-62C	Remembrance	T-59	275.00
CM-63	S. Zedek	T-59	150.00
CM-63a	S. Zedek	S-45	350.00
CM-64	Tel-Aviv-Yafo	T-59	85.00
CM-64a	Tel-Aviv-Yafo	S-59	150.00
CM-64b	Tel-Aviv-Yafo	T-45	60.00
CM-64c	Tel-Aviv-Yafo	S-45	180.00
CM-65	Tourism Award	S-45	275.00
CM-66	8th Zimriya	T-59	18.00
CM-67	Engineers	T-59	60.00
CM-68	Diamond Ind.	T-59	12.00
CM-68a	Diamond Ind.	T-59	35.00
CM-68b	Diamond Ind.	S-59	-R-
CM-68c	Diamond Ind.	S-45	45.00
CM-68d	Diamond Ind.	S-45	90.00
CM-69	Bank Israel	T-59	200.00
CM-69a	Bank Israel	S-34	-R-
CM-70	Fashion	T-59	12.00
CM-71	Metal Ind.	T-59	15.00
CM-73	Ben-Gurion	T-59	-R-
CM-73a	Ben-Gurion	S-59	-R-
CM-74	Benei-Beraq	T-59	250.00
CM-74a	Benei Beraq	S-59	-R-
CM-76	9th Zimriya	T-59	15.00
CM-77	Hassneh	T-59	200.00
CM-77a	Hassneh	S-59	-R-
CM-78	Absorption	S-45	-R-
CM-79	Hobby	T-59	25.00
CM-79a	Hobby	S-45	100.00
CM-80a	Chagall 6 Harp	T-59	400.00
CM-80b	Chagall 6 Harp	SP-59	400.00
CM-81	Canada Park	T-45	12.50
CM-81a	Canada Park	S-45	-R-
CM-82	Chess Olympics	T-59	15.00
CM-83	Jewish Conf.	T-59	15.00
CM-83a	Jewish Conf.	S-59	125.00
CM-84	Israel Appeal	T-59	12.50
CM-85	Mateh Yehuda	T-59	12.50
CM-85a	Mateh Yehuda	S-59	200.00
CM-86	U.J.A.	T-59	12.50

COMMISSIONED MEDALS CONT'D.

CM-86a	U.J.A.	S-59	$100.00
CM-87	Bank Leumi	T-59	25.00
CM-87a	Bank Leumi	S-37	250.00
CM-88	Iraqi	T-59	60.00
CM-88a	Iraqi	S-59	150.00
CM-89	Book Fair	T-59	100.00
CM-90	Petah Tikva	T-59	13.00
CM-90a	Petah Tikva	S-35	45.00
CM-91	Rubinstein II	T-59	12.00
CM-91a	Rubinstein II	S-35	35.00
CM-92	10th Zimriya	T-59	13.00
CM-93	4th Z.O.A.	T-59	13.00
CM-94	Export	T-59	13.00
CM-95	Israel Oil	T-59	13.00
CM-95a	Israel Oil	S-37	90.00
CM-96	Teachers	T-59	13.00
CM-96a	Teachers	S-37	50.00
CM-97	Food Ind.	T-59	12.00
CM-98	Mex. Israel	T-59	12.00
CM-98a	Mex. Israel	S-40	45.00
CM-99	Jer. Meeting	T-45	11.00
CM-99a	Jer. Meeting	S-45	35.00
CM-99b	Jer. Meeting	B-45	45.00
CM-100	Nathanya	T-59	11.00
CM-100a	Nathanya	S-35	40.00
CM-101	Rotary Jub.	T-45	12.00
CM-101a	Rotary Jub.	S-45	55.00
CM-102	Hapoel	T-59	12.00
CM-103	Railways	T-59	11.00
CM-104	K. Hayesod	T-59	11.00
CM-105	Rubinstein III	T-59	10.00
CM-105a	Rubinstein III	S-37	35.00
CM-107	Magen Adom	T-59	11.00
CM-108	Dagon Silo	T-59	11.00
CM-109	Gush Etzion	T-59	11.00
CM-110	Nautical Coll.	T-59	11.00
CM-111	Maccabiah	T-59	11.00
CM-112	Rose Pilgrim.	T-59	11.00
CM-113	Iran-Anniv.	T-59	-
CM-113	Iran-Anniv.	S-45	-
CM-115	Accountants	S-27	22.00
CM-117	Lottery	T-59	10.00
CM-118	L. Insurance	S-37	35.00
CM-119	Rishon Le Zion	T-59	10.00
CM-120	Y. Aliyah	T-59	10.00
CM-121	Diaspora Ed.	T-59	10.00

COMMISSIONED MEDALS CONT'D.

CM-122	S. Freud	T-59	$10.00
CM-123	Tower-David	T-59	10.00
CM-124	Revolt medal	T-59	10.00
CM-125	Precious Stones	S-34	23.00

PRESENTATION MEDALS

PM-1	Sinai	SP-80	-R-
PM-1a	Sinai	SP-80	150.00
PM-2	Nahariya	B-61	12.00
PM-3	Haganah	S-38	50.00
PM-3b	Haganah	B-40	20.00
PM-4	Medical	B-60	175.00
PM-4a	Medical	SP-60	175.00
PM-5	Dentistry	B-33	275.00
PM-6	Philharmonic	B-60	20.00
PM-6a	Philharmonic	S-60	110.00
PM-7	Petroleum	B-59	35.00
PM-8	Paratroops	B-59	310.00

SEASON'S GREETINGS

SG-1	1964	$15.00
SG-1a	1964	25.00
SG-2a	1965	75.00
SG-2b	1965	120.00
SG-2c	1965	55.00
SG-2d	1965	42.00
SG-2e	1965	63.00
SG-2f	1965	135.00
SG-2g	1965	160.00
SG-2h	1965	75.00
SG-2j	1965	65.00
SG-2k	1965	80.00
SG-2m	1965	40.00
SG-2n	1965	100.00
SG-2p	1965	70.00
SG-2q	1965	75.00
SG-2r	1970	-R-
SG-2s	1970	35.00
SG-2t	1965	-R-
SG-3	1966	20.00
SG-4	1967	10.00
SG-5	1968	6.00
SG-6	1969	5.00
SG-7	1970	4.00
SG-8	1971	3.00

SEASON'S GREETINGS CONT'D.

SG-9	1972	$2.00
SG-10	1973	2.00
SG-11	1974	2.00
SG-12	1975 T-I	20.00
SG-12	1975 T-II	2.00
SG-13	1976 T-I	2.00
SG-13	1976 T-II	10.00
SG-14	1977	1.50
SG-15	1978	1.50
SG-16	1979	1.50
SG-17	1980	1.50
SG-18	1981	1.50
SG-19	1983	1.50
SG-20	1984	1.50

A.I.N.A. MEDALS

AM-1	Eshkol	B-50	$15.00
AM-1a	Eshkol	S-45	40.00
AM-2	L.A. Conv.	N-36	12.00
AM-3	Bicent.	B-38	15.00
AM-3a	Bicent.	B-38	15.00
AM-3b	Bicent.	S-38	50.00
AM-3c	Bicent.	S-38	50.00
AM-4	N.Y. Conv.	B-38	15.00
AM-4a	N.Y. set of 2	S-38	-R-
AM-5	L.A. Conv.	P-38	8.00
AM-6	We are Here	B-59	15.00
AM-6a	We are Here	SP-59	25.00
AM-7	10th Anniv.	B-59	15.00
AM-7a	10th Anniv.	S-45	50.00
AM-8	N.Y. Conv.	P-30	10.00
AM-9	13th Anniv.	S-37	30.00
AM-10	N.Y. Conv.	CN-30	5.00
AM-11	N.Y. Forum	CN-30	5.00
AM-12	Bram Dinner	CN-30	5.00
AM-13	Bram-Thanks	CN-30	5.00
AM-14	N.Y. Conv.	CN-30	4.00
AM-15	Bram-Birth.	CN-30	4.00
AM-16	N.Y. Conv.	CN-30	4.00
AM-17	Miami Conv.	CN-30	4.00
AM-18	N.Y. Conv.	CN-30	4.00

A.I.N.A. MEDALS CONT'D.

AM-19	N.Y. Conv.	CN-30	4.00
AM-20	Boston	CN-30	4.00
AM-20a	Boston	GP-30	-R-
AM-21	Miami Conv.	CN-30	4.00
AM-22	N.Y. Conv.	BA-30	4.00

A.I.N.A. MEMBERSHIP MEDALS

AMM-1	1973	$12.00
AMM-2	1974	8.00
AMM-3	1975	3.50
AMM-4	1976	2.50
AMM-5	1977	2.50
AMM-6	1978	2.50
AMM-7	1979	2.50
AMM-8	1980	2.50
AMM-9	1981	2.50
AMM-10	1982	2.00
AMM-11	1983	2.00
AMM-12	1984	2.00

A.I.N.A. SOCIETIES MEDAL

ASM-1	1971	4.00

A.I.N.A. TOUR MEDALS

ANT-1	1969	150.00
ANT-2	1970	200.00
ANT-3	1971	150.00
ANT-4	1972	150.00
ANT-5	1973	165.00
ANT-6	1974	140.00
ANT-7	1975	225.00
ANT-8	1976	150.00
ANT-9	1977	150.00
ANT-10	1978	150.00
ANT-11	1979	150.00
ANT-12	1980	150.00
ANT-13	1981	150.00
ANT-14	1983	10.00
ANT-15	1984	225.00

BANKNOTES

FRACTIONALS

			VF	EF	NEW
1948	50 Mils	FC-1	$50.00	$150.00	$200.00
1948	100 Mils	FC-2	50.00	150.00	200.00
1952	50 Pruta	FC-3	40.00	125.00	265.00
1952	50 Pruta	FC-3a	30.00	65.00	125.00
1952	50 Pruta	FC-3b	25.00	50.00	90.00
1952	50 Pruta	FC-3c	20.00	40.00	80.00
1952	50 Pruta	FC-3d	1.00	3.50	9.00
1952	100 Pruta	FC-4	40.00	80.00	125.00
1952	100 Pruta	FC-4a	25.00	50.00	120.00
1952	100 Pruta	FC-4b	25.00	50.00	115.00
1952	100 Pruta	FC-4c	1.00	3.00	9.00
1952	100 Pruta	FC-4d	800.00	1250.00	2500.00
1953	250 Pruta	FC-5a	6.00	12.00	30.00
1953	250 Pruta	FC-5b	30.00	60.00	90.00
1953	250 Pruta	FC-5c	6.00	10.00	22.00
1953	250 Pruta	FC-5d	15.00	30.00	65.00
1953	250 Pruta	FC-5e	18.00	40.00	75.00

ANGLO-PALESTINE BANK — PALESTINE POUND

1948	500 Mils	BN-1	75.00	150.00	550.00
1948	1 Pound	BN-2	25.00	75.00	125.00
1948	5 Pounds	BN-3	35.00	75.00	135.00
1948	10 Pounds	BN-4	40.00	80.00	175.00
1948	50 Pounds	BN-5	3500.00	5000.00	-R-

BANK LEUMI LE ISRAEL — ISRAEL LIRA

1952	500 Pruta	BN-6	40.00	175.00	475.00
1952	1 Lira	BN-7	12.00	30.00	50.00
1952	5 Lirot	BN-8	25.00	50.00	110.00
1952	10 Lirot	BN-9	30.00	60.00	150.00
1952	50 Lirot	BN-10	550.00	950.00	1300.00

BANK OF ISRAEL — ALEF ISSUE — ISRAEL LIRA

1955	500 Pruta	BN-11	6.00	12.00	40.00
1955	1 Lira	BN-12	4.00	9.00	30.00
1955	5 Lirot	BN-13	5.00	18.00	45.00
1955	10 Lirot-B	BN-14	5.00	18.00	30.00
1955	10 Lirot-R	BN-14a	6.00	19.00	40.00
1955	50 Lirot-B	BN-15	30.00	50.00	90.00
1955	59 Lirot-R	BN-15a	35.00	65.00	125.00

BANKNOTES (CONT'D.)

BANK OF ISRAEL — BET ISSUE — ISRAEL LIRA   NEW

1958	½ Lira	BN-16	$3.00
1958	1 Lira-B	BN-17	2.00
1958	1 Lira-R	BN-17a	2.00
1958	1 Lira-BR	BN-17b	1.00
1958	5 Lirot	BN-18	3.00
1958	10 Lirot-B	BN-19	4.00
1958	10 Lirot-BL	BN-19a	4.00
1958	10 Lirot-R	BN-19b	4.00
1958	10 Lirot-BR	BN-19c	2.00
1960	50 Lirot-B	BN-20	20.00
1960	50 Lirot-R	BN-20a	20.00
1960	50 Lirot-BL	BN-20b	10.00
1960	50 Lirot-G	BN-20c	10.00
1960	50 Lirot-BR	BN-20d	8.00

BANK OF ISRAEL — GIMEL ISSUE — ISRAEL LIRA

1968	5 Lirot-B	BN-21	1.00
1968	5 Lirot-R	BN-21a	1.00
1968	10 Lirot-B	BN-22	2.00
1968	10 Lirot-BL	BN-22a	2.00
1968	10 Lirot-G	BN-22b	2.00
1968	50 Lirot-B	BN-23	6.00
1968	50 Lirot-BL	BN-23a	6.00
1968	100 Lirot-B	BN-24	10.00
1968	100 Lirot-R	BN-24a	10.00
1968	100 Lirot-B	BN-24b	10.00
1968	100 Lirot-BR	BN-24c	10.00

BANK OF ISRAEL — DALET ISSUE — ISRAEL LIRA

1973	5 Lirot	BN-25	1.00
1973	10 Lirot	BN-26	1.50
1973	50 Lirot	BN-27	3.50
1973	100 Lirot	BN-28	7.00
1975	500 Lirot	BN-29	10.00

BANKNOTES (CONT'D.)

BANK OF ISRAEL — HEY ISSUE — SHEQEL

The 1, 5, 10, 50 and 100 Sheqalim banknotes were dated "1978" and "1979" but were issued in 1980.

					FACE
			NEW	ISSUE	8/84
1978	1 Sheqel	BN-30	$1.00	$0.25	$0.003
1978	1 Sheqel	BN-30a	1.00	0.25	0.003
1978	5 Sheqalim	BN-31	1.25	1.25	0.015
1978	10 Sheqalim	BN-32	1.50	2.50	0.030
1978	50 Sheqalim	BN-33	3.00	12.50	0.150
1978	50 Sheqalim	BN-33a	10.00	12.50	0.150
1978	50 Sheqalim	BN-33b	10.00	12.50	0.150
1978	50 Sheqalim	BN-33c	3.00	12.50	0.150
1958	50 Sheqalim	BN-33d	3.00	12.50	0.150
1979	100 Sheqalim	BN-34	4.00	5.00	0.300
1979	100 Sheqalim	BN-34a	4.50	5.00	0.300
1982	500 Sheqalim	BN-35	5.00	30.00	1.500
1983	1000 Sheqalim	BN-36	6.00	10.00	3.000
1983	1000 Sheqalim	BN-36a	6.50	10.00	3.000
1984	5000 Sheqalim	BN-37	15.00	15.00	15.000

ISRAEL SHEQEL VALUE IN U.S. CURRENCY 1980

February 24, 1980 . . . . $0.250
March, 1981 . . . . 0.11000
January, 1982 . . . . 0.06000
December, 1983 . . . . 0.01000
August, 1984 . . . . 0.00355
September 17, 1984 . . . . 0.00253
November 18, 1984 . . . . 0.00190
December 11, 1984 . . . . 0.00175

CORRECTIONS AND ADDITIONS

The Israel Government Coins & Medals Corporation announced new issue prices on medals, to be in effect on January 29, 1984.

GOLD		SILVER	
35 mm.	$520.00	45 mm.	$40.00
30 mm.	200.00	37 mm.	30.00
22 mm.	87.00	34 mm.	21.00
18 mm.	70.00	27 mm.	18.00
13 mm.	36.00		

TOMBAC		CUPRO-NICKEL	
45-59 mm.	9.00	45 mm.	6.00
70 mm.	11.00		

Please make necessary adjustments in the 1979 Edition and the 1982 Supplement for all medals still available.

There are extensive corrections to be made in the 1979 Edition, as the Israel Government Coins & Medals Corporation has issued new final mintages for most all of the coins and medals. These revisions and corrections will all appear in the next Full Edition 1985-1986. New Photos will be used where necessary at that time.

ALL PRICE EVALUATIONS ARE TAKEN FROM COMPILED
DEALERS LISTS AND AUCTIONS CATALOGUES — 1984

1982 SUPPLEMENT

Page 31 One Agora A1-19 1978 CORRECTED MINTAGE: 8,864,000
Page 32 Half-Lira A50-17 1979 CORRECTED MINTAGE: 21,391,170
Page 32 Five Lirot A500-2 1979 CORRECTED MINTAGE: 5,646,428 Jerusalem
   32,000,000 Australian
   <u>37,646,428</u>

Page 39 MS-22a Issued by the Bank of Israel and distributed by the Israel Government Coins & Medals Corporation, Ltd.

Page 41 MS-24 Issued by the Bank of Israel and distributed by the Israel Government Coins and Medals Corporation, Ltd.
FINAL MINTAGE: MS-24   30,217

Page 42	CORRECTED MINTAGE:	H-14	31,612	H-14a	19,040
Page 43	CORRECTED MINTAGE:	H-15	23,774	H-15a	15,448
Page 44	FINAL MINTAGE:	H-16	16,135	H-16a	11,205
Page 45	CORRECTED MINTAGE:	A-22	24,128	A-22a	16,122
Page 47	FINAL MINTAGE:	A-24	16,337	A-24a	11,358
Page 48	CORRECTED MINTAGE:	SI-4	14,489	SI-4a	12,250
	UNDER OBVERSE:	Hebrew date should read "5741"			

CORRECTIONS AND ADDITIONS (CONT'D)

1982 SUPPLEMENT

Page 49   CORRECTED MINTAGE: G-15   6,401
          WEIGHT should read: 17.28 gm.

Page 50   CORRECTED MINTAGE: G-16   7,489
          OBVERSE DATE should read: "5741"

Page 51   FINAL MINTAGE: G-17   5,651

Page 53   FINAL MINTAGE: SM-60   3,165   SM-60a   2,627

Page 54   FINAL MINTAGE: SM-61b   15,349
          CHANGE ISSUE PRICE: SM-61c to $390.00

Page 56   FINAL MINTAGE: SM-63   3,059

Page 58   ADD TO BOTTOM OF LISTING:

No.	Metal	Issue Year	Diam. mm.	Wt. gm.	Final Mintage	Issue Price
SM-64f	gold/750	1984	18	4.4		$85.00

Page 59   ISSUE PRICE SHOULD READ: $11.00

Page 61   FINAL MINTAGE: SM-67   2,680

Page 67   ADD TO BOTTOM OF LISTING:

No.	Metal	Issue Year	Diam. mm.	Wt. gm.	Final Mintage	Issue Price
CM-91c	gold/917	1983	35	30		$595.00

Page 70   FINAL MINTAGE: CM-100   3,374   CM-100a   1,823

Page 71   FINAL MINTAGE: CM-101   1,772   CM-101a   1,473

Page 72   FINAL MINTAGE: CM-102   1,998

Page 73   FINAL MINTAGE: CM-103   4,441

Page 74   FINAL MINTAGE: CM-104   4,491

Page 75   ADD TO BOTTOM OF LISTING:

No.	Metal	Issue Year	Diam. mm.	Wt. gm.	Final Mintage	Issue Price
CM-105b	gold/916.6	1984	35	30		$520.00

Page 76   DELETE NOTE ON BOTTOM: "These medals etc..."
          CHANGE: CM-106a from TOMBAC to... silver-plated.
          FINAL MINTAGE: CM-106a   10

CORRECTIONS AND ADDITIONS

1982 SUPPLEMENT

Page 78 FINAL MINTAGE: CM-108   4,802

Page 81 FINAL MINTAGE: CM-111   4,535

Page 83 WRONG POSITIONING ON AM-9 CORRECT TO FOLLOWING:

No.	Metal	Issue Year	Diam. mm.	Wt. 85.	Final Mintage
AM-9	silver	1981	37	12.44	300

Page 84 WRONG PHOTO: SEE photo replacement page.
REVERSE description wrong. NEW COPY BELOW.
In the centre, a stylized panorama of reunified Jerusalem with outstanding landmarks in a free composition. To the right, the inscription, "Jerusalem," in Hebrew and English. Around the rim the inscription, "Greetings from Jerusalem Israel," in English. In Hebrew, "And you shalt rejoice in thy festival."
(See SG-18 Obv.)

Page 85 WRONG PHOTO: SEE photo replacement page.

Page 88 TOP PARAGRAPH CORRECT THIRD LINE:
(LIRA .0258 - Sheqalim .258)
ADD TO DATES: 5740-1980, 5742-1982, 5743-1983
ADD TO ISSUED CIRCULATION: 500 Sheqalim, Dec. 1, 1982
                                  1000 Sheqalim, Nov. 17, 1983
ADD TO DOTS FOR THE BLIND: 500 Sheqalim has a 3 mm. circle
                                  1000 Sheqalim has a triangle.

Page 89 ADD NEW LISTING FORMAT:

No.	Serial No.
BN-30 With code	Black (10 numbers)
BN-30a Fluorescent with code	Black (10 numbers)

Page 90 ADD NEW LISTING FORMAT:

No.	Serial No.
BN-31 Fluorescent	Black (10 numbers)

Page 91 ADD NEW LISTING FORMAT:

No.	Serial No.
BN-32 With code	Black (10 numbers)

Page 92 ADD NEW LISTING FORMAT:

No.		Serial No.
BN-33	Without bars - Fluorescent with code	Black (10 numbers)
BN-33a	Two green bars - Fluorescent without code	Black (10 numbers)
BN-33b	Four black bars - Fluorescent without code	Black (10 numbers)
BN-33c	Without bars - Fluorescent without code	Black (10 numbers)
BN-34c	Without bars - Non-Fluorescent with code	Black (10 numbers)

UNDER DESIGNER: Delete first sentence: "Designed by graphic artist Mr. Paul Kor. Mr. Adrian Senter, the Italian banknote designer, prepared the designs for printing." Second sentence should read: "Dutch artists prepared the design and engraved the portrait and other features."

CORRECTIONS AND ADDITIONS

1982 SUPPLEMENT

Page 93 ADD TO BN-34: Fluorescent without code
ADD TO BN-34a: Fluorescent without code
UNDER THE BOTTOM PHOTO: Delete the numbers 1 & 2
REPLACE the 2 with an (a)

PHOTO CORRECTIONS FOR PAGES 84-85

FOR AMM-9 replacement   FOR ASM-1 replacement

PAGE 84   PAGE 85

Sheqel Series

THE ISRAEL SHEQEL VALUES IN U.S. CURRENCY 1980

February 24, 1980 . . . . 0.25
March, 1981 . . . . 0.11
January, 1982 . . . . 0.06
December, 1983 . . . . 0.01
August, 1984 . . . . 0.00355
September 17, 1984 . . . . 0.00253
November 18, 1984 . . . . 0.00190
December 11, 1984 . . . . 0.00175

Sheqel-Argorot Coins 1980-

On Feb. 24, 1980 — the new trade coins of Israel were released. The first four denominations were put into circulation and each was equal to ten of the "old agora" series. The new coins bear a value still expressed as "Agora," a minor unit adopted in 1960. The coins distinguish "old" from "new" by their full denomination, "Agorot Hadashot" in the plural and "Agora Hadasha" singular. The coins are substantially smaller in size than the "old agora" they replace.

Five more denominations were added, the one Sheqel and five Sheqalim on Sept. 10, 1981, the ten Sheqalim on Feb. 25, 1982, the fifty Sheqalim on March 8, 1984, and the one hundred Sheqalim on May 2, 1984.

The Sheqel series dated 5742 (1982) contains the letter "He" denoting "5000" like the Victory coin — SI-I. Prior to 1982, the coins bore the abbreviated year, omitting the letter "He." It is presumed this practice will continue on all future issues. All of the "old agora" coins will be withdrawn from circulation and cease to be legal tender.

The Sheqel series has been struck at various foreign mints as well as the Government Mint in Jerusalem: Berne, Canada, Chile, Paris, Rome and Stuttgart.

ONE AGORA (See old 10 Agorot)

OBVERSE
Incuse square with rounded corners, showing to the right, a seven-branched palm tree with two clusters of dates. "Israel" in Hebrew characters below, and in Arabic to the left.

REVERSE
The numeral "1" in the centre, with the words, "Agora Hadasha" and the year in Hebrew characters underneath.

Issued: Feb. 24, 1980
Metal: Aluminum   Plain edge
Diameter: 15 mm.   Weight: .06 gm.

FIVE AGOROT (See old ½ Lira)

OBVERSE
The emblem of the State of Israel; the seven-branched Menorah, between two olive branches joined at the bottom by the word "Israel" in Hebrew characters. "Israel" in Arabic on the right and in Latin letters on the left.

REVERSE
The numeral "5" in the centre, with the words, "Agorot Hadashot" and the year in Hebrew characters underneath.

Issued: Feb. 24, 1980
Metal: Aluminum   Milled edge
Diameter: 18.50 mm.   Weight: .09 mg.

20

TEN AGOROT (See old 1 Lira 1967-)

OBVERSE
Representation of three pomegranates. To the lower left, the emblem of the State of Israel. "Israel" in Hebrew, Arabic and Latin around the rim.

REVERSE
In the centre, the numeral "10," with the words, "Agorot Hadashot" and the year in Hebrew characters underneath.

Issued: Feb. 24, 1980
Metal: Aluminum-bronze   Milled edge
Diameter: 16 mm.   Weight: 2.1 gm.

HALF-SHEQEL (See old 5 Lirot 1978-)

OBVERSE
In the centre, the famed roaring lion of Megiddo. Above, the emblem of the State of Israel. The word "Israel" in Arabic and Latin on the left rim and below the lion, in Hebrew.

REVERSE
The numeral "½" flanked by two eight-pointed starbursts. Below, the word, "Sheqel" and the year in Hebrew characters underneath.

Issued: Feb. 24, 1980
Metal: Cupronickel (75% copper, 25% nickel)   Milled edge
Diameter: 20 mm.   Weight: 3.0 gm.
Rim: A hexagonal appearance is created by the six-sided inner rim.

ONE SHEQEL

OBVERSE
A pearl-rimmed ceremonial chalice, with the Hebrew inscription above, "Sheqel Israel." Design taken from the Shekel of the War of the Jews against Rome 66-70 C.E.

REVERSE
In the centre, the numeral "1" with the word "Sheqel" in modern Hebrew to the left. Above, the emblem of the State of Israel, the Menorah. Around the rim, the word "Israel" in Hebrew, Arabic and Latin, and the date in Hebrew.

Issued: Sept. 10, 1981
Metal: Cupronickel (75% copper, 25% nickel)
Diameter: 23 mm.   Weight: 5.0 gm.
Edge: Intermittently reeded, four segments reeded and five segments plain.

FIVE SHEQALIM

OBVERSE
In the centre, a double cornucopia with pendant ribbon, styled after the motif appearing on coins issued during the reign of John Hyrcanus I (135-104 B.C.E.) On the left, the emblem of the State of Israel, the Menorah. On the right, in Hebrew, Arabic and Latin, the word, "Israel."

REVERSE
In the centre, the numeral "5" with the word "Sheqalim" below in Hebrew and Latin characters. The date in Hebrew characters, below. On either side, two starbursts, copied from the coins during the rule of Alexander Jannaeus (103-76 B.C.E.)

Issued: Sept. 10, 1981
Metal: 92% copper, 6% aluminum, 2% nickel
Diameter: 24 mm.   Weight: 6.1 gm.
Edge: Intermittently reeded (about 94)
Designer: Obv: Eliezer Weisshoff   Rev. Nathan Karp

22

TEN SHEQALIM

The ten Sheqalim is designed to replace the Bank of Israel note of the same denomination which portrays Dr. Theodor Herzl.

OBVERSE
In the centre, an ancient galley with a high aphlaston right, and battering ram left. The galley has a rudder, five oars and a cabin on deck. This is a stylized form of a galley appearing on the coins of Herod Archelaus (4 B.C.E.-6 C.E.). Above the emblem of the State of Israel, the Menorah. Around the rim, the word "Israel" in Hebrew, Arabic and Latin characters.

REVERSE
In the centre, the numeral "10" with the word "Sheqalim" below in Hebrew and Latin characters. The date in Hebrew characters below on the rim. On either side two starbursts, copied from the coins during the rule of Alexander Jannaeus (103-76 B.C.E.)

Issued: Feb. 25, 1982
Metal: Cupronickel (75% copper, 25% nickel)
Diameter: 26 mm.   Weight: 8.0 gm.
Edge: Plain   Designer: Gabriel Neumann

TEN SHEQALIM SPECIAL ISSUES

A special issue of the 10 Sheqalim was released on Nov. 1, 1983. The obverse is the same as the regular 10 Shaqalim. The reverse was modified and commemorates the Hanukka Festival.

REVERSE — HANUKKA VARIETY (With regular obverse)
In the centre, the numeral "10" with the word "Sheqalim" ·below in Latin and Hebrew characters. The date (1984) below in Hebrew "5744." On either side two starbursts. On the bottom rim, the word, "Hanukka" in Latin and Hebrew characters, separated by a Hanukka candelabra (Menorah). Designer: Gabriel Neumann

A special issue of the 10 Sheqalim was released on Jan. 10, 1984. The reverse is the same as the regular 10 sheqalim. The obverse bears the effigy of Dr. Theodor Herzl. The 10 Sheqalim banknote on which Dr. Herzl appears, is being withdrawn. (See BN-32)

OBVERSE — HERZL VARIETY (With regular reverse)
A uniform background formed by the repetition of the word "Herzl" in Hebrew characters. A silhouette of Dr. Herzl, cutting through the background. The word, "Israel" in Latin, Hebrew and Arabic characters, around the right side. The emblem of the State of Israel on the upper left side. Designer: Gabriel Neumann
Dated (1984) "5744" on the reverse

FIFTY SHEQALIM

The Fifty Sheqalim is designed to replace the Bank of Israel note of the same denomination which portrays David Ben-Gurion. (See BN-33)

OBVERSE
In the centre, a replica of the ancient coin issued during the Jewish War against Rome, 66-70 C.E. A lulav flanked by two etrogim with knobs on top, bearing the date, "Year Four," the edge is beaded. To the left, the State emblem. On the botton rim, the word, "Israel" in Hebrew, Arabic and English.

REVERSE
In the centre, the numeral "50" with the word "Sheqalim" below in Hebrew and Latin characters. The date in Hebrew characters below on the rim. On either side two starbursts, copied from the coins during the rule of Alexander Jannaeus (103-76 B.C.E.)

Issued: March 8, 1984
Metal: 92% copper, 6% aluminum, 2% nickel
Diameter: 28 mm   Weight: 9.0 gm.
Edge: Milled
Designers: Obv: Gabriel Neumann   Rev: Nathan Karp
Engravers: Victor Huster   Tidhar Dagan

Note: The reverse of the ancient coin depicted here is a chalice. The legend reads, "Of the Redemption of Zion." The inscriptions are in ancient Hebrew script on this silver coin. The lulav is tied by bands with myrtle branches and willow, as it is the tradition during the Feast of Tabernacles until the present day. The fourth year of the Jewish War against Rome is 69/70 C.E.

ONE HUNDRED SHEQALIM

The one-hundred Sheqalim was released to circulation in Israel on May 2nd, 1984. The coin is intended to gradually replace the 100 Sheqalim banknotes, with the portrait of Ze'ev Jabotinski. (See BN-34). The replacement of a banknote by a coin is more economical, as the minting of a coin is cheaper than the printing of a banknote and it has a much longer life span.

OBVERSE

In the centre, a replica of an ancient "pruta" bronze coin dating from the last of the Hasmonean Kings, Mattathias Antigonus (40-37 B.C.E.). The seven-branched candelabrum with a flat base, against a background of sculptured or ornamental stones, as seen in old Jewish synagogues. The State emblem above to the left. Around the rim, the word, "Israel" in Hebrew, Arabic and English.

REVERSE

In the centre, "100" in bold numerals. Below, in Hebrew and English "Sheqalim." On the left rim, the date in Hebrew.

Metal: 75% copper, 25% nickel   Diameter: 29 mm.
Weight: 10.8 gm.
Designers: OBV: Nathan Karp   REV: Gabriel Neumann
Edge: Slant-structured wide and deep reeds.

Sheqel Series

ONE NEW AGORA HADASHA

No.	Year		Mint	Mintage
AH1-1	1980(5740)		Canada	*110,000,000
AH1-2	1981(5741)		Canada	1,000,000
AH1-2a*	1981(5741)	Piefort-Proof	Berne	30,217
AH1-3	1982(5742)		Stuttgart	1,000,000
AH1-3a*	1982(5742)	Piefort-Proof	Rome	
AH1-4	1983(5743)			(None Minted)
AH1-4a*	1983(5743)	Piefort-Proof	Rome	
AH1-5a*	1984(5744)	Piefort-Proof	Rome	

*Note: In 1982, 90,000,000 were melted from an original mintage of 20,000,000.

*See "Official Mint Sets"

FIVE NEW AGOROT HADASHOT

No.	Year		Ming	Mintage
AH5-1	1980(5740)		Canada	69,532,000
AH5-2	1981(5741)		Canada	1,000,000
AH5-2a*	1981(5741)	Piefort-Proof	Berne	30,217
AH5-3	1982(5742)		Stuttgart	5,000,000
AH5-3a*	1982(5742)	Piefort-Proof	Rome	
AH5-4	1983(5743)			(None Minted)
AH5-4a*	1983(5743)	Peifort-Proof	Rome	
AH5-5a*	1984(5744)	Piefort-Proof	Rome	

*See "Official Mint Sets"

TEN NEW AGOROT HADASHOT

No.	Year		Mint	Mintage
AH10-1	1980(5740)		Canada	167,932,000
AH10-2	1981(5741)		Jerusalem	28,160,000
			Stuttgart	123,000,000
			Paris	90,000,000
				*241,160,000
AH10-2a*	1981(5741)	Piefort-Proof	Berne	30,217
AH10-3	1982(5742)		Stuttgart	23,000,000
AH10-3a*	1982(5742)	Piefort-Proof	Rome	
AH10-4	1983(5743)		Jerusalem	2,500,000
AH10-4a*	1983(5743)	Piefort-Proof	Rome	
AH11-5	1984(5744)			

*Note: Final figures after melt down of 70,2000,000 pieces from 1980-1981 mintages.

*See "Official Mint Sets"

HALF-SHEQUEL

No.	Year		Mint	Mintage
AH50-1	1980(5740)		Berne	52,308,000
AH50-2	1981(5741)		Jerusalem	37,976,000
			Paris	15,296,000
				53,272,000
AH50-2a*	1981(5741)	Piefort-Proof	Berne	30,217
AH50-3	1982(5742)		Jerusalem	18,808,484
AH50-3a*	1982(5742)	Piefort-Proof	Rome	
AH50-4	1983(5743)		Jerusalem	250,000
AH50-4a*	1983(5743)	Piefort-Proof	Rome	
AH50-5	1984(5744)			

*See "Official Mint Sets"

ONE-SHEQEL

No.	Year		Mint	Mintage
AH100-1	1981(5741)		Jerusalem	39,970,000
			Paris	99,000,000
			Berne	15,540,000
				154,540,000
AH100-1a*	1981(5741)	Piefort-Proof	Berne	30,217
AH100-2	1982(5742)		Paris	15,850,000
AH100-2a*	1982(5742)	Piefort-Proof	Rome	
AH100-3	1983(5743)		Jerusalem	26,360,200
AH100-3a*	1983(5743)	Piefort Proof	Rome	
AH100-4	1984(5744)			

*Note: See "Official Mint Sets"

FIVE SHEQALIM

No.	Year		Mint	Mintage
AH500-1	1982(5742)		Paris	12,000,000
			Chile	18,000,000
				30,000,000
AH500-1a*	1982(5742)	Piefort-Proof	Rome	
AH500-2	1983(5743)		Jerusalem	994,000
AH500-2a*	1983(5743)	Piefort-Proof	Rome	
AH500-3	1984(5744)			

*Note: See "Official Mint Sets"

TEN SHEQALIM

No.	Year		Mint	Mintage
AH1000-1	1982(5742)		Stuttgart	18,000,000
			Jerusalem	18,084,123
				36,084,123
AH1000-2	1983(5743)		Jerusalem	17,850,750
AH1000-2a*	1983(5743)	Piefort-Proof	Rome	
AH1000-3	1984(5744)		Jerusalem	
AH1000-3a*	1984(5744)	Piefort-Proof	Rome	
AH1000-3b	1984(5744)	Hanukka-Rev.	Jerusalem	
AH1000-3c	1984(5744)	Herzl-Obv.	Berne	

Note: See description for special issues of the 10 Sheqalim Page 24

*Note: See "Official Mint Sets"

FIFTY SHEQALIM

No.	Year	Mint	Mintage
AH5000-1	1984(5744)	Jerusalem	

Note: See "Official Mint Sets"

ONE HUNDRED SHEQALIM

No.	Year	Mint	Mintage
AH10,000-1	1984(5744)	Jerusalem	
		Canada	

Note: See "Official Mint Sets"

MS-24a "OFFICIAL UNCIRCULATED SET — SOUVENIR FROM THE LIRA PERIOD"

Issued in 1981 — Coins from different years.

Issued by the Israel Goverment Coins and Medals Corporation, Ltd.

This set contains seven coins issued during the Lira Period 1960-1980. The 1 and 5 Agorot are in aluminum, the 10 and 25 Agorot are in copper-nickel-aluminum and the ½, 1 and 5 Lirot are in cupro-nickel. The coins are housed in a wallet-type plastic holder containing historical and numismatic information on this dicontinued series of the Lira Period. The coins are all uncirculated — without the "Star of David" and have assorted dates.

NOTE: In March of 1984, the Israel Government Coins and Medals Corp., offered the above sets, from assorted dates — with the "Star of David." These coins come from the singles left over from the "Official Mint Sets." The 5, 10, and 25 Argorot will probably be in cupro-nickel.

Holder: blue
Size: 5-3/4"x4"
Mintage: 2,000
Issue Price: $2.00

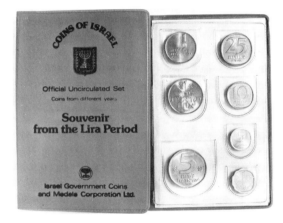

MS-25 "1982 OFFICIAL MINTSET" (Piefort)

Issued by the Israel Government Coins and Medals Corporation, Ltd.

The second set of Piefort Proof coins was minted at the La Zecca Mint, in Rome and commemorates the 34th Anniversary of Israel. The coins have frosted reliefs and are on thicker and heavier blanks. They are marked with the "Star of David" on the reverse. The details of the Piefort Proof coins are the same as in the 1981 issue (MS-24) except for the addition of the new 5 Sheqalim. All coins are dates 5742-1982.

	Diam. mm.	Wt. gr.	Thickness mm.	Edge	Metal
5 Sheqalim	24	13	3.8	milled	92% copper, 8% nickel

The sets are packaged in a card-board holder in booklet form and are plastic coated. The coins are arranged in a circle with the 5 Sheqalim in the centre.

Holder: green-booklet
Size: 4"x5¾"
Mintage:
Issue Price: $11.00

MS-25a "1982 OFFICIAL UNCIRCULATED SET"

Issued by the Israel Government Coins and Medals Corporation, Ltd.

This seven piece set contains all of the coins which circulated in 1982, including the ten Sheqalim which was released on February 25, 1982. The set is presented in an acrylic holder. All coins are uncirculated and without the "Star of David."

Holder: Green
Size: 2⅛"x7⅛"
Mintage:
Issue Price: $3.50

MS-26 "1983 OFFICIAL MINTSET" (Piefort)

Issued by the Israel Government Coins and Medals Corporation, Ltd.

The third set of Piefort Proof coins was minted at the LaZecca Mint, in Rome and commemorates the 35th Anniversary of Israel. The coins have frosted reliefs and are minted on thicker and heavier blanks. (See details in MS-24 ad MS-25). They are marked with the "Star of David" on the reverse. The set includes seven coins dated "1983." (The one and five Agorot were not minted in 1983 for circulation.) This is the first appearance of the 10 Sheqalim in Piefort.

	Diam. mm.	Wt. gr.	Thickness mm.	Edge	Metal
10 Sheqalim	26	16.5	3.9	plain	cupro-nickel

The sets are packaged in a cardboard holder, in booklet form and are plastic coated.

Holder: purple
Size: 4"x5¾"
Mintage:
Issue Price: $11.00

MS-26a "1983 OFFICIAL UNCIRCULATED SET"

Issued by the Government Coins and Medals Corporation, Ltd.

This five piece set includes all of the coins in circulation in 1983. All coins are uncirculated and without the "Star of David." Included in the set are the 10 Agorot, ½ Sheqel, 1 Sheqel, 5 and 10 Sheqalim. They are housed in a transparent acrylic holder.

Holder: plum
Size: 2⅛"x7⅛"
Mintage:
Issue Price: $3.50

MS-27 "1984 OFFICIAL MINTSET" (Piefort)

Issued by the Israel Government Coins and Medals Corporation, Ltd.

The fourth set of Piefort proof coins was minted at the La Zecca Mint, in Rome and commemorates the 36th Anniversary of Israel. The coins have frosted reliefs and are minted on thicker and heavier blanks. The set includes seven coins dated "1984". (The one and five Agorot were not minted in 1984 for circulation). They are marked with the "Star of David" on the reverse.

	Diam. mm.	Wt. gr.	Thickness mm.	Edge	Metal
1 New Agora	15	4.2	2.9	plain	cupro-nickel
5 New Agora	18.5	6.3	2.9	milled	cupro-nickel
10 New Agora	16	4.6	2.9	milled	bronze (red)
½ Sheqel	20	6.8	2.75	milled	cupro-nickel
1 Sheqel	23	11.1	3.5	plain-milled	cupro-nickel
5 Sheqalim	24	13.0	3.8	milled	bronze (yellow)
10 Sheqalim	26	16.5	3.9	plain	cupro-nickel

The sets are packaged in a cardboard holder, in booklet form and are plastic coated.

Holder:
Size: 4"x5¾"
Mintage:
Issue Price: $10.00

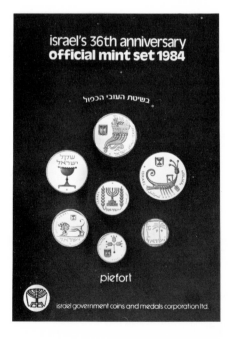

israel's 36th anniversary
official mint set 1984

בשיטת העובי הכפול

piefort

israel government coins and medals corporation ltd.

"Yemen Lamp" 5743 (1982)

HANUKKA COINS H-17

For the first time, the Bank of Israel issued two silver coins to commemorate the Hanukka Festival. The coins depict a 19th century lamp from Yemen, carved in stone. Yemenite Jewry was one of the earliest communities in exile. They suffered severe persecution under Muslim rule — but they maintained contacts with the Jewish centers, and the Land of Israel. The mass immigration of Yemenite Jewry, 100 years ago, was inspired by the verse: "I said, I will rise as a date-palm." (Song of Songs 7.8). With the establishment of the State of Israel, all of the Jews of Yemen came to Israel.

OBVERSE
In the centre, the numeral "1" and "Sheqel" in Hebrew; or "2" and "Sheqalim" in Hebrew. Above, the State emblem. Around the bottom rim, the word "Israel" in Hebrew, English and Arabic, and the date "1982" and its Hebrew equivalent "5743".

REVERSE
In the centre, a Hanukka lamp from Yemen. A 19th century stone candelabrum on a background of Yemenite hand-crafted work. Around the top rim, in Hebrew, "Hanukkiya from Yemen — I will rise as a date-palm." The lamp is displayed in the Israel Museum in Jerusalem.

Metal:	.850 silver	Edge:	1 Sheqel — plain UNC
Diameter:	1 Sheqel — 30 mm.		2 Sheqalim- milled PROOF
	2 Sheqalim — 37 mm.	Mem:	2 Sheqalim —
Weight:	1 Sheqel — 14.4 gm.		Obv: bottom-rim-center
	2 Sheqalim — 28.8 gm.	Star:	1 Sheqel —
Mints:	1 Sheqel — Monnaie		Obv: bottom-rim-center
	de Paris, France	Designer:	Ze'ev Lippmann
	2 Sheqalim, The Mint of	Engraver:	Tidhar Dagan
	Stuttgart, Germany		

		Final Mintage	Issue Price
H-17	1 Sheqel — UNC	14,491	$14.75
H-17a	2 Sheqalim — PROOF	9,000	29.95

"Prague Lamp" 5744 (1983)

HANUKKA COINS H-18

The Bank of Israel issued two silver coins to commemorate the Hanukka Festival. The coins depict a 18th century lamp from Prague. In the heart of Europe, in the ancient capital of the Czech kings, stands the Jewish community of Prague, one of the earliest and, at times, the largest of Jewish communities in this part of the world. There are proofs of a permanent Jewish settlement in Prague from the second half of the 10th century. In 1270, construction of the Altneuschul (the "Old-New Synagogue") was completed, the oldest Synagogue in Europe, it is still in use to this day. At the time of the Nazi invasion of Czechoslavakia, there were about 56,000 Jews living in Prague. There were few survivors of the death camps. Today, the Prague community numbers less than 3,000 Jews.

OBVERSE

In the centre, the numeral "1" and "Sheqel" in Hebrew and English; or "2" and "Sheqalim" in Hebrew and English. On the bottom rim, the emblem of the State of Israel. The sides of the coin are decorative work from the Hanukka Lamp. Around the rim, the word, "Israel" in Hebrew, English and Arabic and the date "1983" and its Hebrew equivalent "5744".

REVERSE

In the centre, an ornate Hanukka Lamp from Prague, (from the Israel Museum collection). The images of Moses and Aaron on either side. Below, in Hebrew, "Hanukkiya from Prague, 18th Century."

Metal:	.850 silver	Edge:	1 Sheqel — plain UNC
Diameter:	1 Sheqel — 30 mm.		2 Sheqalim -milled PROOF
	2 Sheqalim — 37 mm.	Mem:	2 Sheqalim —
Weight:	1 Sheqel — 14.4 gm.		Obv: bottom-rim-center
	2 Sheqalim — 28.8 gm.	Star:	1 Sheqel —
Mints:	1 Sheqel — Monnaie de		Obv: bottom-rim-center
	Paris, France	Designer:	Nathan Karp
	2 Sheqalim — Federal		
	Mint. Berne, Switzerland		

		Final Mintage	Issue Price
H-18	1 Sheqel — UNC		$14.50
H-18a	2 Sheqalim — PROOF	10,894	27.00

"Baron Edmond de Rothschild" 5742 (1982)

34th ANNIVERSARY OF INDEPENDENCE A-25

The two Sheqalim coin was issued by the Bank of Israel and dedicated to the memory of Baron Rothschild. Rothschild is remembered as "The Father of the Jewish Settlement" in Israel. He did more than any other single individual to establish and give practical support to Jewish settlements in the Land of Israel. These settlements were to become the foundation on which the State of Israel was built. Baron Rothschild was a practical visionary who believed that the essence of Torah was based on physical sustenance. The continuation of survival. (See G-18 for gold issue).

OBVERSE
In the centre, the State Emblem. Below, in Hebrew and English, "Baron de Rothschild 1845-1934." Around the outer rim, in Hebrew and English, "Centenary of His First Settlement Activities in Eretz Israel." In the inner rim, "Israel" in Hebrew, Arabic and English, and the date "1982" and its Hebrew Equivalent "5742," and the denomination in Hebrew, "Two Sheqalim."

REVERSE
A high-relief sculptured portrait of Baron Rothschild, facing front. On the left, in Hebrew, "Father of the Jewish Settlements."

Metal:	.850 silver	Edge:	In Hebrew, the incuse
Diameter:	37 mm.		inscription, "Thirty-fourth
Weight:	28.8 gm.		Year of the State of Israel."
Designer:	Obv: Zvi Narkiss	Mem:	Obv: bottom-rim-center
	Rev: Oswald Adler	Star:	Obv: bottom-rim-center
Mints:	UNC: Monnaie de Paris,	Engravers:	Obv: Tidhar Dagan
	France		Rev: Oswald Adler and
	PROOF: Mint of Munich,		Lellya Zuaf David
	Germany		(Sculpture)

		Final Mintage	Issue Price
A-25	UNC	13,335	$23.00
A-25a	PROOF	9,555	39.00

"Year of Valour" 5743 (1983)

35TH ANNIVERSARY OF INDEPENDENCE A-26

The "Year of Valour" celebrated Israel's 35th Anniversary of Independence and also commemorated Israel's Defense Forces 35th Anniversary, (known as the I.D.F.). The I.D.F. is a citizens army and protects Israel's territorial integrity and its sovereign rights. It serves as a guardian of the democratic principles cherished by the People of the Book. Since 1948, the I.D.F. has fought the War of Independence, the Sinai Campaign, the Six-Day War, the War of Attrition, the Yom Kippur War, and the "Peace for Galilee War." The I.D.F. is a pioneer and forerunner in the field of volunteer work. This is the first issue by the Bank of Israel for two coins of different denominations for the Anniversary series. (See G-20 for gold issue and CM-62 for a medal issue.)

OBVERSE

In the centre, the numeral "1" and "Sheqel" in Hebrew and English, or "2" and "Sheqalim" in Hebrew or English. On the left, the State emblem of Israel. Around the rim, the word, "Israel" in Hebrew, Arabic and English, and the date "1983" and its Hebrew equivalent 5743."

REVERSE

In the centre, a sculptural "Star of David" with the I.D.F. emblem superimposed; a sword and an olive-branch in the centre, and the word "Zahal" in Hebrew below, on the bottom rim.

Metal:	.850 silver	Edge:	In Hebrew the incuse
Diameter:	1 Sheqel — 30 mm.		script, "Thirty-fifth Year of
	2 Sheqalim — 37 mm.		the State of Israel.
Weight:	1 Sheqel — 14.4 gm.	Mem:	2 Sheqalim — Obv:
	2 Sheqalim — 28.8 gm.		bottom-rim-center
Designers:	Obv: Gideon Keich	Star:	1 Sheqel — Obv:
	Rev: Ya'akov Zim		bottom-rim-center
Mint:	Mint of Stuttgart,	Engravers:	Obv: Tidhar Dagan
	Germany		Rev: Victor Huster

		Final Mintage	Issue Price
A-26	1 Sheqel — UNC		$18.00
A-26a	1 Sheqalim — PROOF	10,000	40.00

"For We Are Kinsman" 5744 (1984)

36TH ANNIVERSARY OF INDEPENDENCE A-27

The 36th Anniversary commemorative coin celebrates the "Double Chai," (signifies 36, with the Hebrew word 'Chai' symbolizing both the number 18, and life). The theme aims at strengthening the awareness of brotherhood, unity and mutual love among all mankind. Brotherhood and love of one's fellow-man are the binding elements of an orderly society. The precept, "You shall love your neighbor as you love yourself" is the essence of the Bible and the quality of life. "One of the most important things the Holy One, Blessed be He, asks of his children is mutual love and respect." (Tanna De-Bei Eliyahu, 20). The concepts "love, brotherhood, peace and friendship" may seem very demanding but all that is required is a little openheartedness and a cheerful countenance. (See G-22 for gold issue and A-20 for another "Brotherhood" issue).

OBVERSE
In the centre, the State emblem of Israel. Around the rim, the numeral "1" or "2" with the word "Sheqel" or "Sheqalim" in Hebrew and English. The date "1984" and its Hebrew equivalent "5744" on either side. The word "Israel" in Hebrew, English and Arabic, on the top rim.

REVERSE
A filigree likeness of branches and roots over the entire background. The Hebrew words, "Achvat Yisrael" — Brotherhood, in the centre.

		Edge:	In ancient Hebrew script,
Metal:	.850 silver		"Thirty-sixth Anniversary
Diameter:	1 Sheqel — 30 mm.		of the State of Israel. " In
	2 Sheqalim — 37 mm.		English, "For We Are
Weight:	1 Sheqel — 14.4 gm		Kinsman." (Gen. 13.8)
	2 Sheqalim — 28.8 gm.	Mem:	2 Sheqalim — Obv: center
Designer:	Yitzhak Pugacz		under emblem
Mints:	1 Sheqel — UNC, Paris	Star:	1 Sheqel — Obv: center
	Mint, France		under emblem
	2 Sheqalim — PROOF		
	Stuttgart Mint, Germany	Engraver:	Tidhar Dagan

		Final Mintage	Issue Price
A-27	1 Sheqel — UNC		$19.00
A-27a	2 Sheqalim — PROOF		37.00

"Qumran Caves" 5743 (1982)
SI-5

These "Special Issue" coins were issued by the Bank of Israel, and launches a new series of coins called, "HISTORIC SITES IN THE HOLY LAND." They will feature historical sites in the Land of Israel. The Qumran Cave coins feature the cliffs at Qumran and immortalizes the most ancient and important biblical manuscripts —The Dead Sea Scrolls, which were discovered in the caves in the Judean Desert. Two hundred of the manuscripts discovered in these caves are Biblical and several apparently date back almost to the period of the Bible's original manuscript. The Dead Sea Scrolls are kept in the Shrine of the Book in the Israel Museum in Jerusalem. (See G-19 for gold issue and BN-19 for a banknote issue).

OBVERSE

In the centre, the numeral "½" or "1" with the word "Sheqel" in Hebrew and English. The State emblem above. Around the rim, the word "Israel" in Hebrew, Arabic and English, and the date "1982" and its Hebrew equivalent "5743." The coins have 12 sided edges symbolizing the 12 signs of the Zodiac.

REVERSE

The Hever Cliffs, with the caves, where the Scrolls were discovered. The word, "Qumran" in Hebrew and English on the top rim, against a background of ancient script from the Scrolls.

Metal:	.850 silver	Edge:	½ Sheqel — smooth
Diameter:	½ Sheqel — 23 mm.		1 Sheqel — milled
	1 Sheqel — 30 mm.	Mem:	1 Sheqel — Obv:
Weight:	½ Sheqel — 7.2 gm.		bottom-rim-center
	1 Sheqel — 14.4 gm.	Star:	½ Sheqel — Obv:
Mints:	½ Sheqel — UNC Paris		bottom-rim-center
	Mint, France	Designers:	Obv: Eliezer Weisshoff
	1 Sheqel — PROOF		Rev: Dan Gelbart
	Munich Mint, Germany	Engravers:	Obv: Eliezer Weisshoff
			Rev: Tidhar Dagan

		Final Mintage	Issue Price
SI-5	½ Sheqel UNC	15,154	$10.00
SI-5a	1 Sheqel PROOF	9,000	25.00

Note: The Hebrew date contains the letter "Hey" denoting the "5000." This will be used on all future issues.

"Herodion" 5744 (1983)
SI-6

This is the second issue by the Bank of Israel in "Historic Sites in the Holy Land," series. It commemorates the "Mountain-Fortress-Palace" which Herod constructed in the heart of the Judean Desert. Here he shut himself up and found shelter from both his real and imaginary pursuers, and it is very likely that this is the site where he is buried. Herod, a Jew of Edomite origin, reigned as King of Israel, under Roman patronage, for 33 years (from 37 B.C.E. until 4 B.C.E.). He excelled in organizing and developing his kingdom, and carried out numerous building projects both within his country and outside of it, including the Temple in Jerusalem, the port city of Caesarea, fortresses such as Masada and Cypros, as well as theatres and hippodomes — which earned him the title of "The Builder King." On top of a natural hill, Herod erected a 90 foot high circular structure. The massive fill of earth and gravel heaped up against its walls created a cone shaped, artificial mountain. An exotic palace was built deep in the centre of this "crater." (See SG-21 for gold issue).

OBVERSE

In the centre, the numeral "½" or "1" with the word "Sheqel" in Hebrew and English. The State emblem above. Around the rim, the word "Israel" in Hebrew, Arabic and English, and the date "1983" and its Hebrew equivalent "5744." The coins have 12 sided edges, (See SI-5)

REVERSE

The site of the Herodian as seen from an aerial photograph, showing the Judean Hills, the palace, with the sun shining overhead. The word, "Herodian" in English on the left and in Hebrew on the right, divided by the sun.

Metal:	.850 silver	Edge:	½ Sheqel — smooth
Diameter:	½ Sheqel — 23 mm.		1 Sheqel — milled
	1 Sheqel — 30 mm.	Mem:	1 Sheqel — Obv:
Weight:	½ Sheqel — 7.2 gm		bottom-rim-center
	1 Sheqel — 14.4 gm	Star:	½ Sheqel — Obv:
Designer:	Dan Gelbart		bottom-rim-center
Mint:	Munich Mint, Germany	Engravers:	Obv: Tidhar Dagan
			Rev: Victor Huster

		Final Mintage	Issue Price
SI-6	½ Sheqel UNC	11,051	$11.00
SI-6a	1 Sheqel PROOF	10,379	24.95

"The Kidron Valley" 5745 (1984)
SI-7

This is the third issue by the Bank of Israel in "Historic Sites in the Holy Land," series. It commemorates the Kidron Valley and its monuments: Absalom's Pillar, the Cave of Jehoshaphat, the Pyramid of Zecharia, and the sons of Hezir Tomb. The Kidron Valley, or the Valley of Jehosphaphat forms the gentle slope between the Temple Mount and the City of David and the Mount of Olives. Today, the scenery in and around this valley offers a glimpse of ancient Jerusalem, for the valley remains almost totally untouched by modern development. Absalom's Pillar features a stylistic blending of Ionic columns with Doric frieze and Egyptian cornice. Absalom is the son who rebelled against his father, King David. The Sons of Hezir Tomb is also known as the Grotto of St. James. The tomb features two Doric columns and a Doric frieze with triglyphs. The Pyramid of Zecharia is entirely hewn into rock and is an impenetrable structure. No entrance has yet been found. The Cave of Jehospaphat is known as the future site of the Judgement of Nations.
(See G-23 for gold issue).

OBVERSE

In the centre, the numeral "½" or "1" with the word "Sheqel" in Hebrew and English. The State emblem above. Around the rim, the word "Israel" in Hebrew, Arabic and English, and the date "1984" and its Hebrew equivalent '5745." The coins have 12 sided edges, (See SI-5).

REVERSE

The Kidron Valley Monuments stressing Absalom's Tomb. Olive trees allude to the Mt. of OLives (Gethsemane). In the background, the hills of Jerusalem and the wall of the Old City. On the top rim in Hebrew and the bottom rim in English, "Valley of Kidron."

Metal:	.850	Edge:	½ Sheqel — smooth
Diameter:	½ Sheqel — 23 mm.		1 Sheqel — milled
	1 Sheqel — 30 mm.	Mem:	1 Sheqel — Obv:
Weight:	½ Sheqel — 7.2 gm.		bottom-rim-center
	1 Sheqel — 14.4 gm.	Star:	½ Sheqel — Obv:
Designers:	Obv: Ze'ev Lippmann		bottom-rim-center
	Rev: Dan Gelbart	Engraver:	Tidhar Dagan
		Mints:	½ Sheqel — UNC Paris Mint, France
			1 Sheqel — PROOF Stuttgart Mint, Germany

		Final Mintage	Issue Price
SI-7	½ Sheqel UNC		$11.00
SI-7a	1 Sheqel PROOF		24.00

"Baron Edmond de Rothschild"
5742 (1982)
GOLD G-18

The eighteenth gold coin issued by the Bank of Israel was dedicated to Baron de Rothschild in memory of the establishment of farming settlements in the Land of Israel. This became a lifework to which he lent all of his great talents and wealth. Rothschild had one of the most illustrious names in Europe. (See A-25 for silver issue and further details).

OBVERSE

In the centre, the State emblem. Below in Hebrew and English, "Baron de Rothschild 1845-1934." Around the outer rim, in Hebrew and English, "Centenary of His First Settlement Activities in Eretz Israel." In the inner rim, "Israel" in Hebrew, Arabic and English, and the date "1982" and its Hebrew equivalent "5742," and the denomination in Hebrew, "Ten Sheqalim."

REVERSE

A high-relief sculptured portrait of Baron Rothschild, facing front. On the left, in Hebrew, "Father of the Jewish Settlements."

Metal:	.900 gold	Edge:	milled
Diameter:	30 mm.	Mem:	Obv: bottom-rim-center
Weight:	17.28 gm.	Engravers:	Obv: Tidhar Dagan
Designers:	Obv: Zvi Narkiss		Rev: Oswald Adler and
	Rev: Oswald Adler		Lellya Zuaf David
Mint:	Royal Canadian Mint, Ottawa		(Sculptor)

		Final Mintage	Issue Price
G-18	PROOF	4,930	$369.00

"Qumran Caves" 5743 (1982)
GOLD   G-19

The nineteenth gold coin was issued by the Bank of Israel. This is the first issue in a new series that will feature historical sites in Israel. The Dead Sea Scrolls were discovered in 1947 near the Dead Sea in the Qumran Caves. These manuscripts constitute the most important archeological discovery ever made in Israel, and indeed one of the most important of this kind in the world. (See SI-5 for silver issue and BN-19 for banknote issue).

OBVERSE

In the centre, the nominal value "5," with the world "Sheqel" in Hebrew and English on the left. The State Emblem, above. Around the rim, the word "Israel" in Hebrew, Arabic and English, and the date "1982" and its Hebrew equivalent "5743." The coin has 12 sided edges symbolizing the 12 months of the year, and 12 signs of the zodiac.

REVERSE

The Hever Cliffs, with the caves, where the Scrolls were discovered. The word, "Qumran" in Hebrew and English on top rim, against a background of ancient script from the scrolls.

Metal:	.900 gold	Edge:	milled
Diameter:	22 mm.	Mem:	Obv: bottom-rim-center
Weight:	8.63 gm.	Engravers:	Obv: Eliezer Weisshoff
Designers:	Obv: Eliezer Weisshoff		Rev: Tidar Dagan
	Rev: Dan Gelbart		
Mint:	Munich Mint, Germany		

		Final Mintage	Issue Price
G-19	PROOF	4,942	$180.00

"Year of Valour" 5743 (1983)
GOLD — G-20

The twentieth gold coin was issued by the Bank of Israel and is dedicated to the 35th Anniversary of Israel's Defense Forces (I.D.F.). The I.D.F. was officially created about two weeks after the Proclamation of Independence of the State of Israel. It is a true and stable support, a source of strength and of pride for Israel's citizens and the Jewish people throughout the world. The I.D.F. plays an important role in settlement, immigration and absorption, immigrant integration, promotion of national awareness, and education and professional training for youths from underprivileged backgrounds. Protected by the I.D.F.'s scrupulous and rapid execution of security missions, Israel's citizens lead regular, productive and creative lives. (See A-26 for silver issue and CM-62 for a medal issue).

OBVERSE
In the centre, the numeral "10" covering the entire field. Superimposed over the "0" the State emblem, above; and the word "Sheqalim" in Hebrew and English below. Around the rim, the word, "Israel" in Hebrew, Arabic and English and the date "1983" and its Hebrew equivalent "5743."

REVERSE
In the centre, a sculptural "Star of David" with the I.D.F. emblem superimposed; a sword and an olive-branch in the centre, and the word "Zahal" in Hebrew below, on the bottom rim.

Metal:	.900 gold	Edge:	milled
Diameter:	30 mm.	Mem:	Obv: Bottom-rim-center
Weight:	17.28 gm.	Engravers:	Obv: Tidhar Dagan
Designers:	Obv: Gideon Keich		Rev: Victor Huster
	Rev: Ya'acov Zim	Mint:	Federal Mint
			Berne, Switzerland

		Final	Issue
G-20	PROOF	3,382	$398.00

"Herodian" 5744 (1983)

GOLD G-21

The twenty-first gold coin was issued by the Bank of Israel and is the 2nd issue in the "Historic Sites in the Holy Land" series. It commemorates the "Mountain-Fortress Palace" of King Herod. Herod's palace consisted of a spacious reception room, the royal quarters, a Roman style bathhouse and a courtyard surrounded by columns. Deep water wells were hewn out of the slopes of the mountain side. At the foot of the mountain, was an enormous palatial city, where another palace, twice as large as the first, stood among magnificent exotic gardens, storehouses, service buildings, and the seat of the regional administration. At its very heart was an immense pool 135'x210', in the centre — an island pavilion for entertaining guests, that was reached by small sailing boats. Herod's tomb was certainly nearby, but its actual location has yet to be discovered. (See SI-6 for silver issue).

OBVERSE

In the centre, the nominal value "5," with the word "Sheqalim" in Hebrew and English, on the left. The State emblem, above. Around the rim, the word, "Israel" in Hebrew, Arabic and English, and the date "1983" and its Hebrew equivalent "5744." The coins have 12 sided edges, (See G-19)

REVERSE

The site of the Herodian as seen from an aerial photograph, showing the Judean Hills, the palace, with the sun shining overhead. The word "Herodian" in English on the left and in Hebrew on the right, divided by the sun.

Metal:	.900 gold	Edge:	milled
Diameter:	22 mm.	Mem:	Obv: bottom-rim-center
Weight:	8.63 gm.	Engravers:	Obv: Tidhar Dagan
Designer:	Dan Gelbart		Rev: Victor Huster
Mint:	Munich Mint, Germany		

		Final Mintage	Issue Price
G-21	PROOF	4,352	$200.00

"For We Are Kinsman" 5744 (1984)

GOLD G-22

The twenty-second gold coin was issued by the Bank of Israel to commemorate brotherhood, following contemporary events, with the aim of strengthening the awareness of brotherhood, unity and mutual love among all mankind. "When all men will love one another, and show kindness to one another, will mutually aid each other, then all hands will be united as one hand reaching to the Gates of Heaven. Natural brotherhood and selfless love, devoid of personal calculations and self-interest are needed by all mankind today more than ever." (Simcha Raz). (See A-27 for silver issue and A-20 for another "Brotherhood" issue).

OBVERSE

In the centre, the State emblem. Around the rim, the numeral "10" with the word "Sheqalim" in Hebrew and English, and the date "1984" and its Hebrew equivalent "5744" on either side, and the word "Israel" in Hebrew, English and Arabic, on the top rim.

REVERSE

A filigree likeness of branches and roots over the entire background. The Hebrew words, "Achvat Israel" — Brotherhood, in the centre.

Metal:	.900	Edge:	milled
Diameter:	30 mm.	Mem:	Obv: center
Weight:	17.28 gm.		under emblem
Designer:	Yitzhak Pugacz	Engraver:	Tidhar Dagan
		Mint:	Royal Canadian Mint, Ottawa

		Final Mintage	Issue Price
G-22	PROOF		$375.00

"The Kidron Valley" 5745 (1984)

GOLD G-23

The twenty-third gold coin was issued by the Bank of Israel to commemorate the Kidron Valley and is the third issue in the "Historic Sites of the Holy Land" series. The Kidron Valley, or the Valley of Jehoshaphat (also called the "Valley of Fire"), forms the slope between the Temple Mount and the Old City of Jerusalem. Among the few structures are four sepulchres — the Kidron Valley Monuments. Absalom's Pillar is the largest and most imposing monument. The Cave of Jehosphaphat, adjoining Absalom's Pillar contains a subterranean network of tombs and an entranceway decorated in the style of Jewish ornamentation of the Second Temple period. The Sons of Hezir Tomb is the only tomb that can be identified, with an ancient inscription preserved over the cornice, in Hebrew, The tomb and monument of the priests of the family of Hezir. The Pyramid of Zecharia is a monolithic monument in the shape of an Egyptian pyramidal chapel with Ionic columns and half columns and square pillars. (See SI-7 for silver issue and further details).

OBVERSE

In the centre, the numeral "5" with the word "Sheqalim" in Hebrew and English. The State emblem is above. Around the rim, the word "Israel" in Hebrew, Arabic and English, and the date "1984" and its Hebrew equivalent "5745." The coins have 12 sided edges, (See G-19)

REVERSE

The Kidron Valley Monuments stressing Absalom's Tomb. Olive trees allude to the Mt. of Olives (Gethsemane). In the background, the hills of Jerusalem and the wall of the Old City. On the top rim in Hebrew and the bottom rim in English, "Valley of Kidron."

Metal:	.900 gold	Edge:	milled
Diameter:	22 mm.	Mem:	Obv: bottom-rim-center
Weight:	8.63 gm.	Engraver:	Tidhar Dagan
Designers:	Obv: Ze'ev Lippman	Mint:	Berne Mint, Switzerland
	Rev: Dan Gelbart		

		Final Mintage	Issue Price
G-23	PROOF		$175.00

ADDITIONAL MEDAL INDEX

GOLD MEDALS

STATE MEDALS

No.	Issue	Issue Year	Diam. mm.	Wt. gm.	Final Mintage	Issue Price
SM-1	Judaea Capta	1958	27	15	10,000	$30.00
SM-12g	Bar-Mitzvah	1961	27	15	6,975	43.80
SM-12h	Bar-Mitzvah	1961	22	8	6,230	26.25
SM-12j	Bar-Mitzvah	1961	19	5	6,650	18.30
SM-12r	Bar-Mitzvah	1978	30	15	—	200.00
SM-12s	Bar-Mitzvah	1981	22	7	—	87.00
SM-12t	Bar-Mitzvah	1981	13	1.7	—	36.00
SM-21e	Liberation-2	1971	27	15	1,310	43.80
SM-21f	Liberation-2	1971	22	8	1,345	26.25
SM-21g	Liberation-2	1971	19	5	1,335	18.30
SM-29c	Terra Sancta	1963	35	29	4,330	90.00
SM-35b	Masada	1965	27	15	2,880	43.80
SM-35h	Masada	1981	22	7	—	87.00
SM-38b	Rothschild	1966	35	30	3,000	90.00
SM-41b	Balfour	1967	35	30	2,500	90.00
SM-42b	El Al Airlines	1969	35	30	1,900	90.00
SM-43b	Keren Hayesod	1970	35	29	1,645	90.00
SM-48b	Rubinstein-Ist	1974	35	30	1,000	—
SM-48c	Rubinstein-Ist	1975	35	30	2,196	417.00
SM-53b	Technion	1975	35	30	1,918	417.00
SM-54b	Jonathan-Entebbe	1976	35	30	10,873	325.00
SM-56b	Bat-Mitzvah	1978	30	15	—	200.00
SM-56c	Bat-Mitzvah	1981	22	7	—	87.00
SM-56d	Bat-Mitzvah	1981	13	1.7	—	36.00
SM-57d	Wedding	1978	30	15	—	200.00
SM-57c	Wedding	1981	22	7	—	87.00
SM-57d	Wedding	1981	13	1.7	—	36.00
SM-61c	Egypt-Peace	1979	35	30	8,200	200.00
SM-64c	Shema Yisrael	1980	30	15	—	200.00
SM-64d	Shema Yisrael	1980	22	7	—	87.00
SM-64e	Shema Yisrael	1981	13	1.7	—	36.00
SM-64f	Shema Yisrael	1984	18	4.4	—	70.00
SM-66b	Holocaust	1981	30	15	—	200.00
SM-68b	Jewish Settlement	1982	18	4.4	—	70.00
SM-69b	Honor-Elders	1982	18	4.4	—	70.00
SM-71b	Retirees	1982	18	4.4	—	70.00
SM-72b	Mazel Tov — Girl	1982	18	4.4	—	70.00
SM-73b	Mazel Tov — Boy	1982	18	4.4	—	70.00
SM-74b	Am Israel Hai	1982	18	4.4	—	70.00
SM-74c	Am Israel Hai	1984	13	1.7	—	36.00
SM-75b	Tourism	1983	18	4.4	—	70.00
SM-76b	Volunteer	1983	18	4.4	—	70.00

GOLD MEDALS

STATE MEDALS CONTD.

No.	Issue	Issue Year	Diam mm.	Wt. gm.	Final Mintage	Issue Price
SM-77	Jerusalem-Gold	1983	33	7	—	$87.00
SM-78b	Blessed-Healer	1984	18	4.4	—	70.00
SM-79a	Resistance-Nazis	1984	18	4.4	—	70.00
SM-81b	23rd Olympics	1984	30	15	—	200.00
SM-81c	23rd Olympics	1984	22	7	—	87.00

CITY-COIN MEDALS

No.	Issue	Issue Year	Diam mm.	Wt. gm.	Final Mintage	Issue Price
CCM-9b	Jerusalem	1966	35	29	3,000	90.00

HOLY LAND MEDALS

No.	Issue	Issue Year	Diam mm.	Wt. gm.	Final Mintage	Issue Price
HLM-4b	Temple Mount	1982	22	7	—	87.00
HLM-4c	Temple Mount	1982	13	1.7	—	36.00

COMMISSIONED MEDALS

No.	Issue	Issue Year	Diam mm.	Wt. gm.	Final Mintage	Issue Price
CM-8a	Tourism	1962	19	5	380	X
CM-4l7c	Chicago Bank	1972	45	60	25	X
CM-59b	Maariv Daily	1973	35	30	500	X
CM-68e	Diamond T-I	1974	35	29	2,629	417.00
CM-68f	Diamond T-II	1974	35	29	(in above)	417.00
CM-79d	Hobby T-I	1975	22	8	198	X
CM-79e	Hobby T-II	1976	22	8	2,302	X
CM-80	Chagall 6th Harp	1976	35	30	600	X
CM-88b	Iraqi Center	1977	35	30	250	X
CM-91b	Rubinstein 2nd	1983	35	30	1,150	595.00
CM-98b	Mex.-Israel	1979	30	17.3	2,750	175.00
CM-98c	Mex.-Israel	1979	38	34.6	2,050	550.00
CM-105b	Rubinstein 3rd	1984	35	30	—	520.00
CM-113b	Iran-Anniv.	1969	40	30	6,006	X

PRESENTATION MEDALS

No.	Issue	Issue Year	Diam mm.	Wt. gm.	Final Mintage	Issue Price
PM-3a	Haganah	1961	27	15	3,000	X

A.I.N.A. MEDALS

No.	Issue	Issue Year	Diam mm.	Wt. gm.	Final Mintage	Issue Price
AM-3d	Bicentennial	1976	38	—	154	250.00
AM-9a	13th Anniversary	1981	37	15	50	275.00

Jewish Settlements Centenary SM-68

During the first hundred years of "rediscovery" of the Land of Israel, it was the plough that traced our the country's future borders. Although advanced technological industry has gradually gained predominance in Israel, the future of the country will continue to depend on farming communities. There were beginnings before 1882, but the year 1882-83 marked the turning point. Many groups of Jews came to the Holy Land without knowing what lay before them, they founded settlements without roads, transport or means of communication. They laid the foundations of six settlements. Without knowing it, they fixed the borders of the future State. This medal commemorated their dedication. (See SM-28 for further reference).

OBVERSE

Left, a stylized map of Israel, in flowers. Right, in Hebrew and English, "100 Years of Settlement, 1882-1982." Around the right rim, in Hebrew and English, a Biblical passage, "And I will plant them upon Their Land," Amos 9:15.

REVERSE

An image of a ploughshare reflecting the gradual transition from agricultural activities and the development of advanced technological industries. The verse in Hebrew top right, and in English around the left rim, "And dwell in Your Land Safely, Leviticus 25:5."

Edge:	"State of Israel" in Hebrew and English and the Menorah. The silver medals are marked with the word "Sterling .935" in English and "Silver" in Hebrew. Both medals are numerically serialized. The gold medal is milled.
Designers:	Obv: Gideon Keich Rev: Nathan Karp
Mints:	Government Mint, Jerusalem: Silver Moshe Hecht, Tel-Aviv: gold Shelgraph: gold S. Kretschmer & Sons, Jerusalem: tombac and gold

No.	Metal	Issue Year	Diam. mm.	Wt. gm.	Final Mintage	Issue Price
SM-68	tombac	1982	59	98		$9.00
SM-68a	silver	1982	34	22		21.00
SM-68b	gold/750	1982	18	4.4		70.00

Honor the Elders SM-69

In Hebrew, the word signifying an an "old man" is Zaken. It possesses a broader connotation, referring as well to the "learned" ('elder'), the "sage" — thus reflecting the veneration and deference that the Jewish people has always accorded to the elderly. The Torah commands the Jew to "rise up before the hoary head and honor the face of the old man," (Lev. 19:32). This medal now makes it possible for all who so desire to honor older persons with concrete expression of their affection, love, respect and admiration for those who have attained the glory of old age.

OBVERSE
In the centre, a tree with its branches and leaves designed in Hebrew letters forming the verse, "They still bring forth fruit in old age," and "Psalms 92:15" below, also in Hebrew. Around the rim, the legend is repeated in English.

REVERSE
On the background of a tree cross-section, in Hebrew above and in English below, is the verse, "For as the days of a tree shall be the days of My People," Isaiah 65:22.

Edge:	"State of Israel" in Hebrew and English and the Menorah. The silver medals are marked with the word "Sterling .935" in English and "Silver" in Hebrew. Both medals are numerically serialized. The gold medal is milled.

Designer: Gideon Keich   Engraver: Moshe Nov

Mints: Moshe Hecht, Tel-Aviv: tombac and gold
                    Government Mint, Jerusalem: silver

No.	Metal	Issue Year	Diam. mm.	Wt. gm.	Final Mintage	Issue Price
SM-69	tombac	1982	59	98		$9.00
SM-69a	silver	1982	34	22		21.00
SM-69b	gold/750	1982	18	4.4		70.00

Pidyon Haben Silver Medal SM-70

The Pidyon Haben was first issued as a silver coin from 1970 to 1977, when it was discontinued. The new medal features the Redemption of the First Born. Before Sanctuary's completion, the first-born of each household was given to the Creator to serve as a priest and fulfill the spiritual needs of the family and nation as a whole. When the Sanctuary was completed, the Levites and Kohanim, were instructed to act in place of the first-born to fulfill the priestly functions. The Lord then commanded us to redeem our first-born from the obligation to serve. The ceremony is performed of the 31st day following the birth of the first-born son. Five silver shekels are presented by the father to the Kohen, who then returns the child to his parents and declares the son "redeemed." (See Pidyon Haben series for further details PH-1-8).

OBVERSE
In the centre, the Temple vessel, an amphora and five pomegranate flowers are represented the "Five Shekels after the Shekel of the Sanctuary." motifs that appear on the ancient Hebrew coins. Around the rim, a design of seven species found in the Bible.

REVERSE
In the centre, the verse in Hebrew, "Those that are to be redeemed — from a month old shalt thou redeem —by your valuation, five silver shekels, after the shekel of the Sanctuary, Numbers 18.16." On the bottom rim, in English, "Pidyon Haben Medal."

Edge:	"State of Israel" in Hebrew and English and the Menorah. The silver medals are marked with the word, "Sterling .935" in English and "Silver" in Hebrew. The medals are numerically serialized.

Designer: Yizhak Pugacz   Engraver: Tidhar Dagan

Mint: Government Mint, Jerusalem

No.	Metal	Issue Year	Diam. mm.	Wt. gm.	Final Mintage	Issue Price
SM-70	silver	1982	34	22		$21.00
SM-71	set of five with certification in box					100.00

Retirees SM-71

This medal was issued as a token of appreciation for the years of service and association. It was felt by the Israel Government Coins and Medals Corporation that all "retirees" deserve a medal expressing the thanks and respect from their superiors and peers.

OBVERSE
The passage in Hebrew, "And length of days brings understanding, Job 12.12." in stylized letters. The passage is repeated in English around the rim.

REVERSE
Across the center, the inscription in English and Hebrew, "For meritorious Service." Superimposed over the legend is a large tree with stylized roots and fruits.

Edge: "State of Israel" in Hebrew and English and the Menorah. The silver medals are marked with the word, "Sterling .935" in English and "Silver" in Hebrew. The gold medal is milled. The tombac and silver are numerically serialized.

Designer: Asher Kalderon   Engraver: Moshe Nov

Mints: Moshe Hecht, Tel-Aviv: gold and tombac
Government Mint, Jerusalem: silver

No.	Metal	Issue Year	Diam. mm.	Wt. gm.	Final Mintage	Issue Price
SM-71	tombac	1982	59	98		$9.00
SM-71a	silver	1982	34	22		21.00
SM-71b	gold/750	1982	18	4.4		70.00

Mazel Tov — It's A Girl SM-72

With the daughter's arrival into the world, the whole house is filled with charm, grace, beauty and cheer. "Blessed be Thou of the Lord, my daughter." The Jewish father blesses his newborn daughter, as follows:

"O my dove, that are in the clefts of
the rock, in the covert of the cliff,
Let me see thy countenance, let me hear thy voice
For sweet is thy voice and thy countenance is comely."

This medal is the perfect way to express your "Mazel Tov" and is an heirloom to be passed from generation to generation.

OBVERSE

Around the rim, in English, and in the centre in Hebrew, the Biblical passage, "Blessed Be Thou of the Lord my Daughter, Ruth 3.10." On the left, a long stemmed rose bud.

REVERSE

In the centre, within a circle, a representation of the seven species with which Israel is blessed according to the description in Deut. 8.8. "A land of wheat and barley, and vines and fig-trees and pomegranates, a land of olive trees and honey (dates.)" (Bechorim 1.3).

Edge:	"State of Israel" in Hebrew and English and the Menorah. The silver medals are marked with the word, "Sterling .935" in English and "Silver" in Hebrew. Both medals are numerically serialized. The gold medal is milled
Designers:	Obv. Benzion Rotman Engraver: Moshe Nov Rev: Dror Ben-David
Mints:	Moshe Hecht, Tel-Aviv: tombac and gold Government Mint, Jerusalem: silver

No.	Metal	Issue Year	Diam. mm.	Wt. gm.	Final Mintage	Issue Price
SM-72	tombac	1982	59	98		$9.00
SM-72a	silver	1982	34	22		21.00
SM-72b	gold/750	1982	18	4.4		70.00

Mazel Tov — It's A Boy SM-73

The ideal gift to mark the occasion of the birth of a boy or his Brith-Mila is with this special medal. The everlasting memento to commemorate the joyful event is rich in symbolism. "For this child I prayed" said Hannah, the mother of Samuel the Prophet, when the longed-for son was born. Every mother probably experiences this feeling when first seeing her new-born son and again when he is circumcised.

OBVERSE

In the centre, in Hebrew and English, the Biblical passage, "... for this child I prayed, Samuel 1:27." Draped over the right side is a prayer shawl (tallit) with fringe.

REVERSE

In the centre, within a circle, a representation of the seven species with which Israel is blessed according to the description in Deut. 8.8. "A land of wheat and barley, and vines and fig-trees and pomegranates, a land of olive trees and honey (dates)." (Bechorim 1.3).

Edge: "State of Israel" in Hebrew and English and the Menorah. The silver medals are marked with the word "Sterling .935" in English and "Silver" in Hebrew. Both medals are numerically serialized. The gold medal is milled.

Designers: Obv: Nathan Karp   Engraver: Moshe Nov
Rev: Dror Ben-David

Mint: Moshe Hecht, Tel-Aviv: tombac and gold
Government Mint, Jerusalem: silver

No.	Metal	Issue Year	Diam. mm.	Wt. gm.	Final Mintage	Issue Price
SM-73	tombac	1982	59	98		$9.00
SM-73a	silver	1982	34	22		21.00
SM-73b	gold/750	1982	18	4.4		70.00

Am Israel Chai SM-74

These three words, "Am Israel Chai," are full of meaning and give expression to the eternity of the Jewish people. The "burning bush" which was not consumed, depicted on the medal, is symbolic of the endurance of the People of Israel, who despite all hardships, continue to exist. In the verse, "Israel Lives" lies the conviction of the past and the present, and the hope and prayer of the future. The secret of the survival of the nation lies in the three words which have become a promise, a slogan, a song, "Am Israel Chai" — the People of Israel lives on. (See A-9 for further reference).

OBVERSE
In the centre, in Hebrew, "Am Yisrael Chai" is artistically fashioned to enable the medal to be transformed into an original necklace or a peice of jewelry rich in symbolism. On the bottom rim, the English translation, "The People of Israel Lives."

REVERSE
In the centre, a drawing of the "burning bush," a reminder of the promises God made to Moses —that just as the "burning bush" is not consumed, so can no man or nation destroy the people of Israel. Around the rim, in Hebrew and English, "... and the bush was not consumed, Exodus 3:2."

Edge:	"State of Israel" in Hebrew and English and the Menorah. The silver medals are marked with the word "Sterling .935" in English and "Silver" in Hebrew. Both medals are numerically serialized. The gold medal is milled
Designer:	Nathan Karp Engraver: Victor Huster
Mints:	Moshe Hecht, Tel-Aviv: tombac and gold Government Mint, Jerusalem: silver

No.	Metal	Issue Year	Diam. mm.	Wt. gm.	Final Mintage	Issue Price
SM-74	tombac	1982	59	98		$9.00
SM-74a	silver	1982	34	22		21.00
SM-74b	gold/750	1982	18	4.4		70.00
SM-74c	gold/900	1984	13	1.7		36.00
SM-74d	cupro-nickel	1984	30	(key chain)		6.00

Tourist Welcome SM-75

The Holy Land, has been a tourist and pilgrim's attraction for centuries. "And Moses sent them to spy out the land of Canaan to see the land, what it is... whether it be good or bad..." (Numbers 13, 17-19). "And they came to the brook of Eshcol, and cut down from there a branch with one cluster of grapes, and they bore it between two upon a staff..." (Numbers 13:23). Today, three thousand years later, there remains no doubt that the land is "good." It was once the custom to welcome a visitor from afar with "bread and wine" (Genesis 14:18). "Be friendly to the tourist" is not the only message to the people of Israel. Much thought and effort goes into making the Israeli public aware of the delights of being tourists in their own country and the pleasures of touring in Israel. (See CM-8 and CM-65 for previous issues).

OBVERSE
In the left corner, the State emblem. The inscription in Hebrew and English, "Israel welcomes tourist." Below, the emblem of Tourism; a cluster of grapes borne on a staff between two figures.

REVERSE
In the centre, the sun surrounded by a view of settlements and the sea. Around the rim in Hebrew and English, "Visit Israel the miracle on the Mediterranean."

Edge: "State of Israel" in Hebrew and English and the Menorah. The silver medals are marked with the word "Sterling .935" in English and "Silver" in Hebrew. Both medals are numerically serialized. The gold medal is milled.

Designer: Ya'akov Zim   Engraver: Moshe Nov

Mints: Moshe Hecht, Tel-Aviv: tombac and gold
Government Mint, Jerusalem: silver

No.	Metal	Issue Year	Diam. mm.	Wt. gm.	Final Mintage	Issue Price
SM-75	tombac	1983	59	98		$9.00
SM-75a	silver	1983	34	22		21.00
SM-75b	gold/750	1983	18	4.4		70.00

Volunteer Activity SM-76

This medal was issued to commemorate all voluntary services and give official recognition and appreciation to all volunteers who have listened to the "call of conscience," translating moral obligations into actions. To give wholly and whole heartedly, "without receiving a reward," is the essence of volunteer activity for which Jews have always been well-known, and it is the highest of virtues between man and man in Judaism. For the donator of charity gives of his money only, and helps only the poor, while the volunteer gives also of himself (and of his precious time), helping poor and rich alike. In 1972, the Israel Government founded the "Center for Volunteer Services." The Center's motto, "To give is also to receive," expresses the friendship and partnership that develops between the "giver" and the "receiver." (See SM-49 for previous issue).

OBVERSE
In the centre, a chain of hands holding hearts, in the form of a Star of David, expressing the essence of volunteer activity.

REVERSE
In the centre, the emblem of the Center for Volunteer Services in Israel... an out-stretched hand. To the left, in Hebrew and around the rim in English, "Because with a perfect heart they volunteered, Chronicles 1, 29:9."

Edge:	"State of Israel" in Hebrew and English and the Menorah. The silver medals are marked with the word "Sterling .935" in English and "Silver" in Hebrew. Both medals are numerically serialized. The gold medal is milled.

Designer: Dror Ben-David   Engraver: Victor Huster

Mints: Moshe Hecht, Tel-Aviv: tombac and gold
             Government Mint, Jerusalem: silver

No.	Metal	Issue Year	Diam. mm.	Wt. gm.	Final Mintage	Issue Price
SM-76	tombac	1983	59	98		$9.00
SM-76a	silver	1983	34	22		21.00
SM-76b	gold/750	1983	18	4.4		70.00

Jerusalem of Gold SM-77

Jerusalem in Hebrew means "City of Peace." Its chronicles, however, were turbulent and the people whose spiritual genius lent it lustre were carried off into exile time and time again. For generations they cried out: "If I forget thee, O Jerusalem, let my right hand forget its cunning." About three thousand years ago, David, annointed King of Israel, conquered the city and made it his capital. His son Solomon built the First Temple in 953 B.C.E. Nebuchadnezzar of Assyria destroyed the Temple in 587 B.C.E. Half a century later the Jews returned and built the Second Temple which stood until the Romans razed it in 70 C.E. (See CM-123 and SG-20 obv.)

OBVERSE

A stylized panorama of reunited Jerusalem, arranged in a free composition. The word, "Jerusalem" in Hebrew and English on the right. (Same reverse of SM-46.).

REVERSE

In the centre, a lion advancing, a symbol of the city, encircled by the word "Jerusalem" in twenty different languages.

Edge: "State of Israel" in Hebrew and English and the Menorah. In English, "G 585" and the serial number.

Designers: Obv: Ya'akov Zim   Engraver: Tidhar Dagan
                Rev: Nathan Karp

Mint: Moshe Hecht, Tel-Aviv

No.	Metal	Issue Year	Diam. mm.	Wt. gm.	Final Mintage	Issue Price
SM-77	gold/585	1983	22	7.0		$87.00

Blessed Be The Healer SM-78

This medal was issued to be given as a loving gift expressing appreciation for the good work of those in whose hands our health lies. Someone visiting a sick person and who does not want to come empty-handed, can emphasize his good wishes by giving the patient this medal. Doctors and nurses who assist men and women in their time of sickness are thus charged with an errand of mercy — charged by the Healer of all flesh (Jerusalem Talmus, Ketuboth, 13). It is a Jewish custom on seeing a friend who has recovered from an illness, to recite the blessing: "Blessed be the Healer of the Sick," (Simcha Raz). The medal conveys to a sick person — wishes for a speedy recovery. It constitutes an expression of gratitude to the devoted doctor or nurse, and for someone who has recovered from his illness, it conveys feliciations and joy.

OBVERSE

In the centre, a stylized design of a sun shining as a symbol of righteousness and healing, with a young branch expressing growth and freshness. Around the rim, in Hebrew and English: "and thy health shall spring forth speedily, Isaiah 58:8."

REVERSE

In the centre, in Hebrew and English, "Blessed be the Healer of the Sick."

Edge:	"State of Israel" in Hebrew and English and the Menorah. The silver medals are marked with the word "Sterling .935" in English and "Silver" in Hebrew. Both medals are numerically serialized. The gold medal is milled.

Designer: Zvi Narkiss   Engraver: Tidhar Dagan

Mints: Moshe Hecht, Tel-Aviv: tombac and gold
              Government Mint, Jerusalem: silver

No.	Metal	Issue Year	Diam. mm.	Wt. gm.	Final Mintage	Issue Price
SM-78	tombac	1984	59	98		$9.00
SM-78a	silver	1984	34	22		21.00
SM-78b	gold/750	1984	18	4.4		70.00

Resistance to the Nazis SM-79

A glorious chapter of heroism was written in the history of the Jewish People by the World War II fighters, men and women who fought the Nazis and their cohorts in the ghettos and sewers of Europe, in the marshes and inside the very death camps. In 1983, the year of "Jewish Heroism," the men and women who fought for human survival and national dignity four decades ago and survived, met in the reborn Jewish State to commemorate, share and celebrate, and reaffirm their vow of, "Never Again." This medal will transmit to future generations the message of taking a proud stand against oppression.

OBVERSE

In the centre, the symbol of the World Assembly to Commemorate Jewish Resistance and Combat against the Nazis. A figure of a man and a woman, armed-grasping a stylized "Star of David" and using it like a shield. Below, the dates "1943-1983" and its Hebrew equivalent, '5703-5743." Around the rim in English and Hebrew, "World Assembly to Commemorate Jewish Resistance and Combat during World War II."

REVERSE

On the right, the emblem of the State. On the top, the symbol of, "The Year of Jewish Heroism and Valour," and in Hebrew, "Resistance Struggle Against the Nazis." Around the rim, in Hebrew and English, "In Quietness and in Confidence shall be your strength, Isaiah 30:15."

Edge:	The gold medal is milled. The cupronickel medal contains, "State of Israel" in Hebrew and English and the Menorah and is numerically serialized
Designer:	Assaf Berg Engraver: Tidhar Dagan
Mints:	Moshe Hecht, Tel-Aviv: cupronickel Credit Gold: gold

No.	Metal	Issue Year	Diam. mm.	Wt. gm.	Final Mintage	Issue Price
SM-79	cupronickel	1984	45	42		$6.00
SM-79a	gold/750	1984	18	4.4		70.00

Purim Medal SM-80

In the word of the Jewish sages; the world is based upon three things: "The Torah, The Temple service, and the practice of charity." Every man, from the age of 13 upwards, rich or poor, or whatever his abode, contributes a half-shekel for the Temple service (thereby demonstrating the equality of all men before the Holy One, Blessed Be He, and the necessity of mutual sharing for the attainment of perfection.) On the Eve of Purim, it is usual to contribute in memory of the Half-Shekel of the Temple service. For this symbolic contribution, congregants usually use a coin or medal with a content of 10 grams pure silver (like the "half-shekel") specially prepared by synagogue officials. This contribution also commemorates the victory of the Jews over the tyrant Haman, when they countered the 10,000 shekels he had paid to King Xerxes for their destruction, by their own shekels. Today the Purim Festival can be marked with the Purim Medal for it contains approximately 11 grams of pure silver and is similar to the ancient Half-Shekel. (See HS-1-2 coins, 1961-1962).

OBVERSE
On the left, a copy of the ancient half-shekel coin. Below, in Hebrew, "In commemoration of the ceremonial half-shekel."

REVERSE
Intertwined Stars of David, expressing the brotherhood of the Jewish People. Below, in Hebrew the passage, "Go gather together all the Jews." Below, on the rim, "Book of Esther, 4:16."

Edge: "State of Israel" in Hebrew and English and the Menorah and "Sterling .925" in English and "Silver" in Hebrew. They are numerically serialized.

Designers: Obv: Ya'akov Enyedi   Engraver: Moshe Nov
            Rev: Asaf Berg

Mint: Government Mint, Jerusalem

No.	Metal	Issue Year	Diam. mm.	Wt. gm.	Final Mintage	Issue Price
SM-80	silver/.925	1984	27	12		$18.00

Note: The medal is supplied in an attractive box and is accompanied by a certificate signed by the two Chief Rabbis of Israel.

The 23rd Olympics in Los Angeles SM81

In honor of the 1984 Olympic Games in Los Angeles, the Israel Government Coins and Medals Corporation issued the first Olympic medal to be issued by the Israel government. The medal is designed to perpetuate the event and the Olympic ideal: "to participate in 8 Olympic Games and to strive to break records, to maintain equality and the sporting spirit." Israel has until now participated in 8 Olympic Games. The Olympics deeply etched in every Israeli heart are those of 1972, in Munich, when 11 athletes and trainers were killed by P.L.O. assassins. The Olympic Games were first held in 776 B.C.E. in Ancient Greece and were held 293 times, and ceased in 293 C.E. In 1896 the Games re-opened in Athens, Greece and the slogan chosen for the Olympics was "Faster, higher, stronger."

OBVERSE

A stylized figure of an athlete in motion. Around the left rim, the inscription in English and Hebrew, "A Life of bodily Vigour."

REVERSE

In the centre, the Israeli Olympic emblem; a candelabra with the 7th arm in the form of the burning-torch, above the symbolic five rings. Below, the word "Israel" in English and Hebrew. Around the rim, in English and Hebrew, "Olympiad Los Angeles 1984" and its Hebrew equivalent "5744."

Edge: "State of Israel" in Hebrew and English and the Menorah. The silver medals are marked "Sterling .935" in English and "Silver" in Hebrew. The gold 30 mm. medal is marked "G 750." The gold 22 mm. medal has a milled edge. All medals not milled are numerically serialized.

Designer: Obv: Dan Reisinger   Rev: Gideon Keich

Engraver: S. Kretschmer & Sons, Jerusalem

Mints: Moshe Hecht, Tel-Aviv: tombac
Government Mint, Jerusalem: silver and gold

No.	Metal	Issue Year	Diam. mm.	Wt. gm.	Final Mintage	Issue Price
SM-81	tombac	1984	70	140		$11.00
SM-81a	silver/.935	1984	37	26		29.00
SM-81b	gold/750	1984	30	15		200.00
SM-81c	gold/585	1984	22	7		87.00
SM-81d	Set of above 4 in box					289.00
SM-81e	cupro-nickel	1984	30 (Key chain)			6.00

Note: The United States Olympic Committee halted the sale of the medal in the U.S. on August 16, 1984. Israel was told they needed authorization from the Committee to be marketed in the U.S. (Perhaps it can be marketed directly from Israel?)

Sir Moses Montefiore   SM-82

On the occasion of the bicentenary of the birth and centenary of the death of Sir Moses Montefiore, and on the initiative of the Jewish Museum in London, the Israel Government issued this State Medal. Sir Moses Montefiore, is the best known British Jew of the 18th Century and is remembered throughout the Jewish world for his journeys to champion oppressed Jews, his philanthropy and his devotion to the Land of Israel. His philanthropy was not limited to Jews and he became a national figure in Britain. His wife, Judith was of great assistance to him in his activities and is depicted on the medal also, Sir Moses Montefiore promoted the education and welfare of the Jewish population in Israel, fostered their employment in agriculture and industry and encouraged Jewish settlements outside the walls of Jerusalem, building the windmill at Yemin Moshe, and used the American Judah Touro's bequest to found the Mishkenot Sha'ananim, originally almshouses. His 100th birthday was celebrated worldwide by Jews and others who venerated the philanthropist, devoted to his religion and his brethren and honoured by his Queen.

OBVERSE

In the centre, sculptured portraits of Sir Moses and Judith Montefiore. Around the rim, in English and Hebrew, ''Moses and Judith 1784-1862 — 1784-1885.''

REVERSE

In the centre, the house of "Mishkenot Sha'ananim," below, its name in Hebrew and English. In the background the windmill of Yemin Moshe in Jerusalem, with trees on the hills behind. Around the rim, the verse in Hebrew and English, "For it is time to favour her for the set time is come. Psalms 102.14."

Edge:	"State of Israel" in Hebrew and English and the Menorah. The silver medals are marked "Sterling .935" in English and "Silver" in Hebrew. The gold 22 mm. medal is milled. The tombac and silver medals are numerically serialized.
Designer:	Obv: Lellya Zuaf David Rev: Ya'akov Zim
Engraver:	Moshe Nov, Tel-Aviv
Mints:	Moshe Hecht: tombac and gold Government Mint, Jerusalem: silver

No.	Metal	Issue Year	Diam. mm.	Wt. gm.	Final Mintage	Issue Price
SM-82	tombac	1984	59	98		$9.00
SM-82a	silver/935	1984	37	26		29.00
SM-82b	gold/585	1984	22	7.0		87.00

70

"Temple Mount" HLM-4

The Temple Mount, the Mount of Moriah, is considered the religious and national centre of the People of Israel. It is the site of the Foundation Stone where the sacrifice of Isaac took place. The first Temple was built there by King Solomon. He placed the Holy of the Holies on the Foundation Stone — the Ark of the Covenant. Seventy years after the destruction of the First Temple by the Babylonians, the Second Temple was built on the same site by the returning exiles; only to be destroyed by the Roman conquerors in 70 C.E. After this destruction, Jews adopted the Western Wall, a remnant of the Wall surrounding the Second Temple as a surrogate site. The Temple Mount remains inviolate as a most holy symbol of Judaism.

OBVERSE
The Western Wall, the Domes of the El Aksa and Dome of the Rock, Mosques (now on the site), in the centre. Above, in Hebrew and English, the inscription, "Temple Mount."

REVERSE
In the centre, a three dimensional rendering of a map of Jerusalem found on a mosaic floor in a Sixth Century Synagogue. The mosaic featured Jerusalem with its walls, towers and many buildings as well as the Temple Mount. Above, in Hebrew and English, the word, "Jerusalem."

Edge: "State of Israel" in Hebrew and English and the Menorah. The silver medals are marked "Sterling .935" in English and "Silver" in Hebrew. The 22 mm. gold medal is marked, "G.585." The above medals are numerically serialized. The 13 mm. gold medal is milled.

Designer: Gideon Keich   Engraver: Tidhar Dagan

Mints: S. Kretschmer & Sons, Jerusalem: tombac and gold 13 mm. Government Mint, Jerusalem: silver and gold 22 mm.

No.	Metal	Issue Year	Diam. mm.	Wt. gm.	Final Mintage	Issue Price
HLM-4	tombac	1982	59	98		$9.00
HLM-4a	silver	1982	37	26		30.00
HLM-4b	gold/.585	1982	22	7		87.00
HLM-4c	gold/.900	1982	13	1.7		36.00
HLM-4d	cupro-nickel	1984	30 (keychain)			6.00

Iran-Pahlavi Coronation Anniversary, 1969 CM-113

This medal was commissioned by the Shah of Iran, Mohammed Riza Pahlavi to commemorate the anniversary of his coronation (1941). On Oct. 26th, the ceremony took place without bloodshed, and is known as the "White Revolution." The anniversary of his coronation was an expression of his success in promoting changes within the economic and social structure of Iran. Which had raised the level of the Iranian people to one of the most progressive nations and restoring his country to the greatness it once occupied in the region. The coronation anniversary was celebrated by the Shah in exile, due to his expulsion.

OBVERSE

On the top, the Shah's royal crown. Below, the Persian inscription, "In memory of the coronation of His Royal Majesty, the King of Kings, Mohammed Riza Pahlavi, the flower of the Pahlavi Kingdom of Iran." Below, the date, "4th of Aban."

REVERSE

In the centre, depicted in five segments, the achievements of the "White Revolution." Starting at 12:00 clockwise: "Dividing the Land for the poor; Nationalizing Industry; Medical Services; Freedom for the Women; and Education." In the centre, a cooperative is depicted. Around the rim, the Persian inscription, enumerates 12 achievements: "Construction; Housing; Medical Services; Land Redistribution; Women's Rights to vote and to be elected; Education and the abolishment of Illiteracy; Nationalization of the Forests; Inclusion of workers in profit-sharing, an opportunity for people to acquire shares in national enterprises; Bureaucratic Reforms; Water Resources serving the people; Social Services; and Improvements in the country's image."

Edge:	Persian inscription, "A gift to the Pahlavi Royal House." Siver medals are marked "Sterling Silver .925." Gold medals "G900," both in English.
Designer:	Shamir Brothers
Engraver:	Arye Sandik, Tel-Aviv
Mint:	Merkur Bank, Germany

No.	Metal	Issue Year	Diam. mm.	Wt. gm.	Final Mintage
CM-113	tombac	1969	59	80	30,005
CM-113a	silver/925	1969	45	40	15,006
CM-113b	gold/900	1969	40	30	6,006
SM-113c	gold/900	1969	59	80	1
CM-113d	silver/925	1969	59	80	1

Pilgrimage to Jerusalem, 1970 CM-114

This medal was issued in 1970 for the Ministry of Tourism. It was commissioned to be awarded to group leaders who brought tourists to Jerusalem during the "Pilgrimage" campaign.

OBVERSE

In the centre, a schematic rendering of the prominent buildings in Jerusalem — religious and secular. Around the rim, in Hebrew on top and below, in English, "Jerusalem."

REVERSE

Blank — the medal is uniface.

Edge: smooth

Designer: "Roli" Rothschild & Lippmann

Engraver: Moshe Nov

Mint: Moshe Hecht, Tel-Aviv

No.	Metal	Issue Year	Diam. mm.	Wt. gm.	Final Mintage
SM-114	tombac	1970	59	100	100

Accountants Association Jubilee, 1981
CM-115

The Association of Accountants was established in Israel on October 5, 1931, the Association consisted of only 46 members. It now represents 3,500 accountants and has had a big influence on the economic administration of Israel. The Association was accepted as an associate in the International Associations of Standards (IASC), the International Federation of Accountants (IFAC) and in the European Organization of Accountants (UEC). The Israel Government Coins and Medals Corporation issued this medal to the subscribers in 1983.

OBVERSE
In the centre, the emblem of the association. On the right, in English and on the left in Hebrew, "1931-1981 / Jubilee / Institute / Of / Certified / Public / Accountants / in Israel."

REVERSE
In the centre, the Hebrew quotation, "For they dealt in good faith, Kings 2:22.7," and again in English around the right rim.

Edge: The letters "I.G.C.M.C." in English and Hebrew and the Menorah. The medals are marked "Sterling .935" in English and "Silver" in Hebrew. They are numerically serialized.

Designers: Obv: Yair Lindenberg   Engraver: Moshe Nov
            Rev: Gideon Keich

Mint: Government Mint, Jerusalem

No.	Metal	Issue Year	Diam. mm.	Wt. gm.	Final Mintage	Issue Price
CM-115	silver	1981	27	12		$18.00

Raphael Retirement, 1982 CM-116

This medal was commissioned by "Raphael" to be used as presentation pieces to those members who retire. The Authority for Development of Weapons, (Raphael in Hebrew), is today the central research and development instrument of the Israeli defence establishment. The Authority develops sophisticated weapons by long range planning. It also is engaged in finding solutions to problems concerning day to day defence operation. (See CM—61 & CM-75 for previous issues).

OBVERSE
In the centre, within a rectangle, the emblem of Raphael. Above, in Hebrew, "Raphael." Around the bottom rim, in Hebrew, "The Authority for the Development of Weapons."

REVERSE
On the right, a stylized emblem of the Israel Defence Forces, an olive-branch and sword. On the left, in Hebrew, the passage, "For with wise advice thou shalt make thy war," below, "Proverbs 24:6."

Edge: The letters I.G.C.M.C." in English and Hebrew and the Menorah. The medals are numerically serialized.

Designer: Submitted by Raphael

Engraver: Moshe Nov

Mint: Moshe Hecht, Tel-Aviv

No.	Metal	Issue Year	Diam. mm.	Wt. gm.	Final Mintage
CM-116	tombac	1982	59	98	

Israel State Lottery, 1983 CM-117

The Israel State Lottery (Mifal Hapayis) is a public undertaking managed by a board of directors whose members consist of representatives of the Government, the central authorities and the general public. It dedicates its income to the development of health, education and welfare institutions. This medal commemorates 30 years of activity by the Mifal Hapayis. (See CM—41 for previous issue). Struck in 1982, but offered to the subscribers in 1983.

OBVERSE

In the centre, a schematic design of buildings surrounded by three figures — a schoolboy, a nurse with a baby in her arms, and an old man leaning on a cane. On the right rim there are seven stars and eight on the left rim. On the top rim, in Hebrew, "Mifal Gapayis for the furthering of education and health." On the bottom rim, in English "Israel / Lottery" separated by the emblem of the Mifal Hapayis.

REVERSE

In the centre, the passage, in Hebrew, "Come and let us cast lots, that we may know" (Torah 1:7). Around the Hebrew passage is the English. Around the rim, the 12 signs of the Zodiac, believed to control the fates of men.

Edge:	The letters "I.G.C.M.C." in English and in Hebrew and the Menorah. The medals are numerically serialized.
Designer:	Dror Ben-David Engraver: Moshe Nov
Mint:	Moshe Hecht, Tel-Aviv

No.	Metal	Issue Year	Diam. mm.	Wt. gm.	Final Mintage	Issue Price
CM-117	tombac	1983	59	98		$9.00

Linked Life Insurance, 1983 CM-118

Linked Life insurance is an original Israeli system of the oldest financial instrument in the world. Many insurance companies in the world looked for ways to guarantee the value of money from life insurance, but found no safer or clearer method to answer the problem of inflation than the one used in Israel — linking life insurance to the cost of living. The government of Israel entered into a contract system with the association of life insurance companies by which the government issues to the insurance companies debt fees linked to the Cost of Living Index, equivalent to the obligation of the insurance company to its insured. This medal commemorates the 25th Anniversary of "Linked Life Assurance."

OBVERSE
Around the rim, in English, the inscription, "25th Anniversary of Linked Life Assurance, 1957-1982" and the Hebrew dates equivalent, "5718-5743." On the right centre, the inscription is repeated in Hebrew without the dates. With the Life Insurance emblem at the beginning. On the left side are irregular lines.

REVERSE
To the right centre, The Life Insurance emblem, a home with people inside. The sheqel coin on top, symbolizes thrift or savings. To the left, the Hebrew quotation, "Israel shall dwell in safety, Deut. 33:28." The same inscription in English on the bottom rim.

Edge: The letters "I.G.C.M.C." in English and Hebrew and the Menorah. The medals are marked "Sterling .935" in English and "Silver" in Hebrew. The medals are numerically serialized.

Designer: Ya'akov Enyedi   Engraver: Moshe Nov

Mint: Government Mint, Jerusalem

No.	Metal	Issue Year	Diam. mm.	Wt. gm.	Final Mintage	Issue Price
CM-118	silver	1983	37	26		$30.00

Rishon Le Zion Centenary, 1983 CM-119

Rishon Le Zion, one of the first six settlements in modern Israel was founded on the 15th of Av, 1882. Its centenary commemorates the merit of the first settlers who contributed to the forging of the State of Israel. The blue and white flag was first hoisted during it's third anniversary celebrations, and later became Israel's national flag. The Israeli national anthem. "HaTikva," (the melody of which was composed by a native of Rishon Le Zion), was first sung there. In 1889, in the shade of the old sycamore tree, in Rishon Le Zion, the Jewish National Fund was created. And it was there that the first wine cellar was established by Baron de Rothschild. (See SM-28 for another issude).

OBVERSE

In the centre, Rishon Le Zion's central synagogue, with a Menorah on top and steps below, within an inner circle. Around the rim, in Hebrew and English, the inscription "Rishon Le Zion 5642-1882."

REVERSE

A kinetic sculpture design. A cluster of grapes against a "Star of David," the form of which changes according to the angle of the view. Below, the signature "Ya'akov Agam," the designer, in Hebrew and English, within a "Star of David" formed by the Hebrew letter "Aleph" (Agam's Hebrew initial) and the English letter "A."

Edge: The letters "I.G.C.M.C." in English and Hebrew and the Menorah. The medals are numerically serialized.

Designer: Ya'akov Agam   Engraver: Victor Huster

Mint: Moshe Hecht, Tel-Aviv

No.	Metal	Issue Year	Diam. mm.	Wt. gm.	Final Mintage	Issue Price
CM-119	tombac	1983	59	98		$9.00

Youth Aliyah 50th Jubilee, 1983 CM-120

The medal was commissioned to commemorate this organization which has provided a healthy environment and good education for generations of children of immigrants, and as of late, even those of Israelis. 1933 saw the beginning of "Youth Aliyah" activities in Germany, when Recha Freier devoted herself to saving Jewish children from the hands of the Nazis. In 1934 the first group of chidren was welcomed to Israel by Henrietta Szold and sent to Kibbutz Ein Harod. Since then, over 200,000 children from all over the world have received their education in Youth Aliyah frameworks. The issue of this medal marks the 50th Jubilee of Youth Aliyah. (See H-3 for further information).

OBVERSE
In the centre, the emblem of the Jubilee, combined with Youth Aliyah's regular emblem: a sawn tree-trunk from which a new branch sprouts, symbolizing renewed growth. It is superimposed over the numeral "50." Below, in English and Hebrew, the dates "1933/4-1983/4." Around the bottom rim, in Hebrew and English, "Youth Aliyah."

REVERSE
In the centre the figures of a boy and a girl reading an open book. Below, in Hebrew and English, the passage "Start a child on the right road, Proverbs 22."

Edge: The letters "I.G.C.M.C." in English and Hebrew and the Menorah. The medals are numerically serialized.

Designer: Izzy Kahana

Mint: Moshe Hecht, Tel-Aviv

No.	Metal	Issue Year	Diam. mm.	Wt. gm.	Final Mintage	Issue Price
CM-120	tombac	1983	59	98		$9.00

Diaspora Education, 1983 CM-121

This medal was commissioned by the Department for Jewish Education and Culture as a symbol for fostering Jewish identity in communities worldwide, linking them with Israel, discouraging assimilation, and encouraging Aliyah. The Department is developing Diaspora Hebrew Kindergarten networks and "Israeli Studies" centers in schools; study trips to Israel for groups of pupils; expansion of advanced course for Hebrew studies teachers; promotion of Hebrew language instruction for adults in Ulpanim; Israeli administration of studies for children of Israelis in the Diaspora; publishing of books for reading and study in easy Hebrew and preparation of audio-visual teaching material. The Department will present this medal to all those active in the Diaspora Jewish and Zionist education, honoring their devotion to this vitally important cause.

OBVERSE

In the centre, the "Star of David," symbol of Judaism, against a globe. A pointer used for reading in the Scroll of Law, symbolizing Jewish education and culture. Below, in Hebrew the passage, "And they went about throughout all the cities of Judah, and taught the people, Chronicles 11,17:9." Around the rim, the English and Spanish translation of the passage.

REVERSE

To the right, the emblem of the Department, a seven-branched candelabra in the form of olive-leaves. To the left, in Hebrew and around the rim in English, the inscription, "The Department for Education and Culture in the Diaspora W.Z.O." (The initials of the World Zionist Organization).

Edge:	The letters "I.G.C.M.C." in English and Hebrew and the Menorah. The medals are numerically serialized.

Designer:	Ya'akov Enyedi	Engraver:	Tidhar Dagan

Mint:	Moshe Hecht, Tel-Aviv

No.	Metal	Issue Year	Diam. mm.	Wt. gm.	Final Mintage	Issue Price
CM-121	tombac	1983	59	98		$9.00

Sigmund Freud, 1983 CM-122

This medal was commissioned by the Israel Psychoanalytic Society to commemorate their 50th Anniversary, and to honor the founder of pyschoanalysis Sigmund Freud. Freud treated hysteria using hypnosis methods and later changed to "free association." His theories roused bitter antagonism, but he greatly influenced anthropology, education, art and literature.

OBVERSE

The portrait of Sigmund Freud facing front. On the bottom rim, his name "Sigmund Freud," in English and Hebrew, separated by the years "1856-1939" (the dates of his birth and death).

REVERSE

In the centre, the number "50" with the "0" containing a human head with a window looking into it. On the top, the Hebrew inscription, "The Anniversary of the Israel Psychoanalytic Society." The same inscription on the bottom in English, and the dates of the anniversary, "1933-1983."

Edge: The letters "I.G.C.M.C." in English and Hebrew and the Menorah. The medals are numerically serialized.

Designer: Gideon Keich   Engraver: Moshe Nov

Mint: S. Kretschmer & Sons, Jerusalem

No.	Metal	Issue Year	Diam. mm.	Wt. gm.	Final Mintage	Issue Price
CM-122	tombac	1983	58	98		$9.00

Tower of David, 1983 CM-123

This medal was commissioned on the opening of the Jerusalem Municipal Museum on the site. "Thy neck is like the Tower of David," as is written in the Song of Songs (4:). The Tower of David nestles on a high point controlling the Old City of Jerusalem. Throughout the history of the City, towers and forts were erected on this spot, with the aim of protecting Jerusalem's western face. In the fortress' courtyard, an impressive remnant of the Hasmonean Wall was found, the first "wall" of the tower. Following the Herodian tower are the remains of the Byzantines, early Arabs, Crusaders, Mamelukes and Ottomans. These remains, illustrate the continuity of settlement in the fortress for more than 2,000 years. Now the "Tower of David" has come to symbolize the reunited city. (See SM-77).

OBVERSE
A silhouette of the Tower of David fortress, superimposed are the words, "Jerusalem City Museum" in Hebrew and English. Around the top rim, "The Tower of David" in English and Hebrew.

REVERSE
In the centre, a lion advancing, a symbol of the City, encircled by the word "Jerusalem" in twenty different languages. (See SG-20 obv.)

Edge: The letters "I.G.C.M.C." in English and Hebrew and the Menorah. The medals are numerically serialized.

Designer: Nathan Karp   Engraver: Tidhar Dagan

Mint: Moshe Hecht, Tel-Aviv

No.	Metal	Issue Year	Diam. mm.	Wt. gm.	Final Mintage	Issue Price
CM-123	tombac	1983	59	98		$9.00

The Revolt Medal, 1984 CM-124

On the 1st of February, 1944 the High Command of the National Military Organization (The Ezel) published its announcement of a revolt, declaring "War to the very end" on British rule in the Land of Israel. The underground began an armed struggle which continued for four years, until the establishment of the State of Israel. There were attacks of Government Offices, police stations, military camps and airfields, including the bomb attack on the civilian and military headquarters in the King David Hotel in Jerusalem. The British reacted by arresting and imprisoning the fighters and those who supported them, expelling them from the country, imposing curfews, setting up detention camps in the towns, and even sentenced some people to death by hanging. This medal serves to mark and commemorate the contribution of the underground that fought to drive out foreign rule, and to establish an independent Jewish State in the Land of Israel. (See SI-4, SM-65, G-16 for issues on Ze'ev Jabotinsky).

OBVERSE
In the centre, the words in Hebrew, "40th Anniversary of the Declaration of the Revolt," on the left, the dates "7th of Shevat 5740/1.2.1944." Within the Zero of "40" is the Ezel Emblem. Beneath, is the symbol of the "Year of Valour," a Star-of-David intertwined with the numeral "35" and the Hebrew word "Israel." On the bottom rim, in Hebrew, "EZEL Congress," (National Military Organization Congress).

REVERSE
In the centre, in Hebrew, "Take up arms and fire," taken from Ezel mentor, Ze'ev Jabotinsky's poem, "Betar," below. On the bottom rim, the Betar emblem — a menorah. On the lower right rim, in Hebrew, "Israel's 35th Independence Day."

Edge: The letters, "I.G.C.M.C." in English and Hebrew and the Menorah. The medals are numerically serialized.

Designer: Ruth Lubin

Engraver: Tidhar Dagan

Mint: Moshe Hecht, Tel-Aviv

No.	Metal	Issue Year	Diam. mm.	Wt. gm.	Final Mintage	Issue Price
CM-124	tombac	1984	59	98		$9.00

Precious Stones Medal, 1984 CM-125

Israel's Precious Stones Industry is considered the leading one in the world due to its technological development and the sophistication of the polishing equipment being used. The historic relationship of Israel with precious stones, their value and symbolism goes back to the breastplate of the High Priest described in our origins. During the last few years Israel advanced and strengthened its position as a producer and supplier of precious stones throughout the world. This medal was used on the occasion of the International Precious Stones Congress, the first event of its kind worldwide. The event took place in Israel with the participation of representatives from twenty-six countries.

OBVERSE

In the centre, in Hebrew and English, "The International Precious Stones Congress Israel 1983." On the top left — their emblem. Around the rim, in English, "Israel Precious Stones & Diamonds Exchange. Israel Emerald Cutters Association."

REVERSE

In the centre, the twelve precious stones on the High Priest's breastplate, in Hebrew, "Ruby, Topaz, Beryl, Turquoise, Sapphire, Diamond, Opal, Agate, Amethyst, Emerald, Onyx, Jasper." Around the rim in English, "And thou shalt make the breastplate of judgement with cunning work... and thou shalt set in it settings of stone, Exodus 28:15."

Edge: The letters, "I.G.C.M.C." in English and Hebrew and the Menorah. "Sterling .935" in English and "Silver" in Hebrew, "Union Bank of Israel." The medals are numerically serialized.

Designer: Ze'ev Lippmann

Engraver: Moshe Nov, Tel-Aviv

Mint: Government Mint, Jerusalem

No.	Metal	Issue Year	Diam. mm.	Wt. gm.	Final Mintage	Issue Price
CM-125	silver/935	1984	34	22		$21.00

Haifa Municipality, 1984 CM-126

Of all cities in Israel, Haifa is unique, having been endowed with a rare combination of the forest clad Mount Carmel and the azure tranquil waters of a natural bay. Haifa is a tri-level city, each level with its endemic characteristics. The upper level comprises residential neighborhoods, entertainment and hotels; the intermediate-established neighborhoods which are gradually turning into business centers; the lower level — partly located on a reclaimed coastline is the heart of the city, with its port and business establishments. The city boasts many special sites such as: The Bahai Garden — The World Center of the Bahai Faith, Elijah's Cave — focus of pilgrimage for believers of all religions, the Carmelit — the only subway of its kind in Israel, and the new cable car which will connect Bat Galim with Stella Maris.

OBVERSE

A panoramic view characteristic of Haifa. With Mt. Carmel in the background covered with trees, the Mediterranean Sea in the foreground with a ship in the bay and the sea wall behind. The Cable car is depicted on the right.

REVERSE

In the centre, the emblem of the City of Haifa, a sailing ship and sea wall behind, below the word "Haifa" in English, Hebrew and Arabic. Around the rim, in English and Hebrew, "... and Carmel be counted for a forest... Isaiah 32:15." Above the city emblem a crown with an olive-branch.

Edge: The letters, "I.G.C.M.C." in English and Hebrew and the Menorah. The silver medals, "Sterling .935" in English and "Silver" in Hebrew. The medals are numerically serialized.

Designer: Hava Merdkovitch

Engraver: Moshe Nov, Tel-Aviv

Mints: Moshe Hecht: tombac
Government Mint, Jerusalem: silver

No.	Metal	Issue Year	Diam. mm.	Wt. gm.	Final Mintage	Issue Price
CM-126	tombac	1984	59	98		$9.00
CM-126a	silver/935	1984	34	22		21.00

A.I.N.A. Membership Medals

AMM-10 1982 (5742) bronze-aluminum 30 mm. **14 gm.** Mint: Cincinnati Coins and Medals, Ohio

OBVERSE
In the centre, the "Star of David" outlined by Roman numerals "XV" (Symbolizing the A.I.N.A. Anniversary) and the Hebrew "Lamed," (or 30), and "Dalet" (or 4) symbolizing Israel's 34th Anniversary. Around the rim, "A.I.N.A.'s 15th Year of Service to its members and Israel Numismatics." On the bottom centre, the date, "1982" and above, it's Hebrew equivalent "5742." Designed by Jacob Hennenberg of Beachwood, Ohio.

REVERSE
In the centre, the emblem of A.I.N.A. surrounded by an American flag at left and an Israeli flag at right. On the bottom centre rim, the initials, "N.S." for the designer, Nat Sobel, of Brooklyn, New York.

Edge: Milled
Mintage: 3,000

AMM-11 1983 (5743) bronze-aluminum 30 mm. **14 gm.** Mint: Cincinnati Coins and Medals, Ohio

OBVERSE
In the centre, an open umbrella. On the top, the initials of "A.I.N.A." Underneath, the date, "1983" and its Hebrew equivalent "5743." On the sleeves of the arms holding the umbrella, the inscriptions, left: "The Shekel / Publications / Youth Programs / Audio-Video / Speakers." On the right: "Study Groups / Conventions / I.N.S. Clubs / Fraternity / Medals." Below, the initials "N.S." for the designer, Nat Sobel. Around the rim, "Numismatics — Metallic Ambassadors of Goodwill." A quote from Yitzak Avni, the former director of the I.G.C.M.C.

REVERSE
In the centre, the emblem of A.I.N.A. surrounded by the American flag at left and an Israeli flag at right. On the bottom centre rim, the initials, "N.S." for the designer, Nat Sobel.

Edge: milled
Mintage: 2,525

A.I.N.A.
Membership Medals

AMM-12 1984 (5744) bronze-aluminum 30 mm. 14 gm. Mint: Cincinnati Coins and Medals, Ohio

OBVERSE
In the centre, a stylized representation of three pomegranates, on the Shekel of the First Revolt (66-70 CE). On the left, the date "1984." Below, on the right, "Israel 36" for their anniversary date, and "A.I.N.A. 17" for their anniversary date. Around the rim, small pearls, graduating in size in two arcs. Designed by Alex Shagin.

REVERSE
In the centre, the emblem of A.I.N.A. surrounded by an American flag at left and an Israeli flag at right. On the bottom centre rim, the initials, "N.S." for the designer, Nat Sobel.

Edge: milled
Mintage: 3,000

1982   None issued

1983   (14)   A.I.N.A. logo on reverse as used on A.I.N.A. 1983 Membership Medal. A rendering of Masada, with the words, "Masada Shall not Fall Again," super-imposed. Above, "We Shall Remain Free Men." Around the rim, "15th Annual Study Tour to Israel, March 3-17, 1983." The initials "M.B." on the left slope, for the designer, Morris Bram.

1984   (15)   A.I.N.A. 1984 membership medal, silver-plated. An incuse "Star of David" overstruck in the field of the pome-granates, on the obverse.

No.	Metal	Issue Year	Diam. mm.	Wt. gm.	Final Mintage
ANT-14	bronze-alum.	1983	30	14	250
ANT-15	bronze-alum.	1984	30	14	75

Season's Greetings

SG-19 5743 (1983) Bronze-nickel 25.4 mm. 5.6 gm. Mint: Cincinnati Coins & Medals, Ohio

Note: There was no 1982 issue.

OBVERSE
Like the HLM-4 Temple Mount Medal. The Western Wall, the Domes of El Aksa and the Dome of the Rock, Mosques, in the centre. Above in Hebrew and English, the inscription, "Temple Mount."

REVERSE
On the right in Hebrew and English, the inscription, "Israel Government Coins and Medals Corporation." On the left, the emblem of the Corporation; the date "1983" below, and its Hebrew equivalent "5743" above.

Edge: milled   Mintage: 70,434

Designers: Obv: Gideon Keich
               Rev: Nathan Karp

SG-20 5744 (1984) Bronze-nickel 25.4 mm. 5.6 gm. Mint: Cincinnati Coins & Medals, Ohio

OBVERSE
Like CM-123 and SM-77 reverses. In the centre, a lion advancing, a symbol of the city of Jerusalem, encircled by the word "Jerusalem" in twenty different languages.

REVERSE
On the right in Hebrew and English, the inscription, "Israel Government Coins and Medals Corporation." On the left, the emblem of the Corporation; the date "1984" below, and its Hebrew equivalent "5744" above.

Edge: milled   Mintage: 70,600

Designer: Nathan Karp

BN-35
FIVE HUNDRED SHEQALIM — 1982

Colour: Ivory/red/green   Size: 76/138 mm. Released Dec. 1, 1982

FACE: Portrait of Baron Edmond de Rothschild; a group of pioneers dressed in period fashions on a background of stylized designs of first settlements. Above, the dates "1982" and the equivalent in Hebrew "5742." On the right edge, in Hebrew, "Baron Edmond de Rothschild 1845-1934." The numeral "500" in the upper left-hand and the lower-right corners. Left, "Bank of Israel — Five Hundred Sheqalim." Below the pioneers, in Hebrew the signatures, "Moshe Mandelbaum — Governor of the Bank:" "Haim Barki — Chairman of the Advisory." Left of the background, four small rhombi, held to the light, they form a "Star of David." Right edge, a small circle (3 mm.) for the blind. Security strip off center. Watermark depicts a portrait of Rothschild.

BACK: A Vine-shrub. Numeral "500" in the upper right-hand and lower left-hand corners; bottom right in Arabic, "Five Hundred Sheqalim; "Sheqalim" also in English. Top-left, "Bank of Israel" in Hebrew and English. Two small rhombi, left of vine. Background consists of the names of the 44 settlements Rothschild founded or assisted, in Hebrew: "Or Akiva, Segra (Ilanit), Ayelet Hashahar, Alumot Beitanya, Ashdod-Yaacov, Beer-Yaacov, Bait Vegan, Beit-Hananya, Beit-Keshet, Benyamina, Bat-Shlomo, Gedera, Ginossar, Givat-Ada, Hazoriim, Zichron-Yaacov, Hadera, Yavniel, Yessod-Hamaala, Kinneret, Kfar Glickson, Kfar Giladi, Kfar Tabor." Lower line, "Meir Shefeya, Mazkeret Batya, Mahanaim, Menahemya, Maagan-Michael, Maavan-Mvi, Mishmar Hashlosha, Mizpeh, Metula, Neve Yam, Nahalat Jabotinsky, Ness-Ziona, Atlit, Pardess-Hanna, Petah-Tikva, Rishon-Le-Zion, Rosh Pinna, Sde Eliezer, Shdemot Deborah, Sdot Yam, Talmei Elazer." Note is plasticized.

Designer: Zvi Narkiss

No.		Serial No.
BN-35	Non-flourescent without code	Black (10 numbers)

BN-36
ONE THOUSAND SHEQALIM — 1983

Colour: Green/pink · Size: 76/138 mm. Released Nov. 17, 1983.

FACE: An effigy of Maimonides against a background of passage from the Halachah "Money Lender and Borrower" from the original manuscript of "Mishneh Torah," chapter 27, with the handwriting and signature of Maimonides. Caption on left edge in Hebrew, "Maimonides Rabbi Moshe Ben Maimon, 1138-1204.". Numeral "1000" in upper left and lower right corners. Lower left corner, in Hebrew, "Bank of Israel" and "One Thousand Sheqalim." Center top, the signatures in Hebrew, "Moshe Mandelbaum, Governor of the Bank of Israel" and "Abraham Yosef Shapira, Chairman of the Advisory Council." The date "1983" and its Hebrew equivalent "5743" below the passage. A triangle lower right — a sign for the blind. A triangle on the left, held up to the light forms a "Star of David." Verticle wave-like lines can be seen in the background representing the lake and springs of Tiberias. A security metal strip off-center.

BACK: Illustration represents the city of Tiberias, where Maimonides is buried. The word, "Tiberia" in English and Hebrew on the edge of the upper left corner. The numeral "1000" in upper right and lower left corners, in Arabic — lower right corner, "1000 Sheqalim" in English and Arabic on the bottom right. "Bank of Israel" in English and Arabic, bottom left. Serial numbers, upper left and lower right. On the lower right is an illustration of the stone Menorah discovered in Tiberias in 1921 in the Hamat-Tiberias Synagogue (2nd or 3rd century). Triangle right. Abstract circles in the background, and a landscape associated with Tiberias. Note is plasticized.

Designer: Zvi Narkiss (Arieh Glazer participated in the design on the back).

Note: On the face — to the right of Maimonides head, reading from the middle upwards, in Hebrew, "Harambam Rarav Moshe Ben Maimos, etc," on BN-36. The correct spelling of Rabbi is "HARAV" the character "HEH" was later printed instead of the "RESH" which spelled "RARAV" incorrectly.

No.		Serial No.
BN-36	"RARAV" Non-fluorescent (Error)	Black (10 numbers)
BN-36a	"HARAV" Non-fluorescent (Correct)	

BN-37
FIVE THOUSAND SHEQALIM — 1984

Colour: White/blue/beige/green   Size: 76/138 mm. Released Aug. 9, 1984

FACE: On the right, a full-face portrait of Levi Eshkol, former Prime Minister of Israel. On the right edge, in Hebrew, "Levi Eshkol Prime minister," and the dates in English "26.6.1963 — 26.2.1969" and in Hebrew. On the top edge, the date in English and Hebrew, "1984-5744." In the top right corner, a square printed in intaglio for the blind. The numeral "5000" in the upper left and lower right corners. The background is a panorama of the City of Jerusalem depicting the unification of the city. Lower left corner, in Hebrew, "Bank of Israel/Five Thousand Sheqalim." Along side, the signatures of "Moshe Mandelbaum, Governor of the Bank," and "Abraham Yosef Shapira, Chairman of the Advisory Board." Above and to the left, of the signatures, tiny geometric forms, when held to the light — forms a tiny Star of David with the geometric form on the back. A security metal strip off-center. Released August 9, 1984

BACK: A water pipe-the national water carrier; meadow and barren land. This illustrates the two domains identified with Mr. Eshkol: the development of water projects and agricultural settlements. The numeral "5000" in the upper right corner, in the lower left "5000 Sheqalim," and the Arabic equivalent on the lower right corner. On the top left corner, "Bank of Israel" in English and Arabic. On the lower left, above the serial numbers, a tiny geometric form, which coincides with the ones on the face. The watermark contains the effigy of Eshkol in the same posture as in the portrait. The note is plasticized for better preservation.

Designer: Ya'akov Zim

No.
BN-37   non-fluorescent

Serial No.
Black (10 numbers)

Bank Note Sets

BNS-3   1978-1983 — "HEY ISSUE"

A set of banknotes comprised of the 50, 100, 500 and 1000 Sheqalim in crisp condition. The seventh issue of the Bank of Israel, depicts portraits of prominent Jewish personalities on the face of the notes: David Ben Gurion, Ze'ev Jabotinsky, Baron Edmond de Rothschild and Maimonides. The banknotes are encased in a laminated wallet.

Issue Price: $25.00

BNS-4   1978 50 SHEQALIM — "HEY ISSUE"

One sheet of 12 banknotes of the 50 Sheqalim. The front depicts the portrait of David Ben Gurion. The back depicts the Golden Gate in the Old City of Jerusalem. (An uncut sheet).

Issue Price: $9.00